The
Yorkshire
Beer
Bible

2nd EDITION

A drinker's guide to all the brewers and beers of God's own country

Simon Jenkins

GREAT NORTHERN

Great Northern Books Limited

PO Box 1380, Bradford, BD5 5FB

www.greatnorthernbooks.co.uk

Every effort has been made to
acknowledge correctly and contact
the copyright holders of material in
this book. Great Northern Books
apologises for any unintentional errors
or omissions, which should be
notified to the publisher.

ISBN: 978-1-912101-06-1

Design and layout: David Burrill

CIP Data

A catalogue for this book is available
from the British Library

Introduction

Perhaps we are getting close to peak beer.

Recent figures suggest the number of breweries opening nationwide has slowed down dramatically. Others have been forced to close, downsize or merge in the face of a fiercely competitive market. Some suggest that those who once had a raging thirst for new beer have begun to tire of its endless novelty, slowly shifting their attentions and affections elsewhere, notably to gin.

I've seen some small evidence of these trends during my travels and discussions with brewers for the preparation of the second edition of this book. Haworth Steam Brewery have gone full steam ahead into distilling gin, though they still make beer too; some breweries of which I had really high hopes, the likes of Bradford and Northallerton, have gone out of business in the two years since the first. Page 173 includes a full list of those no longer with us, and doubtless some will be mourned more deeply than others.

And yet it's been hard to discern any real slow down in the expansion of Yorkshire's brewing scene. The first edition featured 178 breweries and this time we're hovering somewhere around the 200 mark. Among the newcomers are some really exciting and interesting contenders – Spotlight at Snaith, who use beer as a means of raising awareness of various life-limiting genetic conditions; Little Black Dog at nearby Carlton, who can barely keep up with the demand from customers at their Selby taphouse; and Triple Point who have emerged re-invigorated from the ashes of Sheffield's much-loved Sentinel brewhouse.

Beers such as Rasputin Nut Oil, a powerful Imperial Russian Stout brewed on Asylum Harbour's tiny garage brewkit, Korruptd's range

Say hello to...

ROOSTER'S TAPROOM

OPEN
WEDNESDAY
TO
SUNDAY
EVERY WEEK

DOG FRIENDLY

CHILDREN
WELCOME*

SERVING
CASK & KEG
VEGAN-FRIENDLY BEER
WINE, CIDER
GIN & SOFT DRINKS

CHECK OUT OUR LARGE SOUTH-FACING BEER GARDEN

PROUDLY INDEPENDENT
SINCE 1993
Rooster's
HARROGATE
BREWERY & TAPROOM

UNIT H5, FIFTH AVENUE, HORNBEAM PARK, HARROGATE, HG2 8QT

FOR OPENING HOURS & MORE INFORMATION VISIT
WWW.ROOSTERS.CO.UK/TAPROOM-INFO

*UNDER 14'S WELCOME UNTIL 7PM. U18'S TO BE SUPERVISED AT ALL TIMES

of saisons, stouts and Hopfenweisses and St Mars' genre-busting Jack D'Or give the lie to any suggestion that we are losing our taste for novelty. All of these beers come from new businesses, trading with vigour, imagination and confidence.

So, in Yorkshire at least, beer continues to flourish. Though I played no part in it save for chronicling its progress, the growth of beer culture has given today's drinkers a host of taste experiences unimaginable just a few years ago. Where once Yorkshire drinkers might have been content to find on a bar a single Tetley handpump standing as a reliable guarantor of quality, now they are beguiled by bewildering choice.

Licensed premises have changed too. Bars focussed on serving quality beer – whether on cask or keg, from the UK or further afield – have revitalised Britain's on-trade. Longer-established pubs have expanded their own repertoire to compete.

That there has proved to be a market for such variety has encouraged brewers to stretch out into styles which had once been forced to the margin – porters and stouts, fruit beers, milds and braggots – confident that there were drinkers out there, thirsty both for refreshment and enlightenment. India Pale Ale, once a niche product of a handful of brewers, has ballooned into a global phenomenon, fuelled by dazzling citric hop varieties from the USA.

The stigma once attached to keg beers has been blown away by brewers demonstrating that crafted, quality beer can be dispensed this way, while cans have displaced bottles to become the packaging of choice for many new brewers targeting the off-trade, a move unthinkable a decade or so ago.

This book aims to demonstrate Yorkshire's sizeable contribution to this new world order. I set out with the intention of including every single brewery in the county, though I apologise if some have slipped through the net.

During my travels, I asked several brewers to offer a definition of craft beer. My most satisfactory answer came from renowned Yorkshire brewer Dave Sanders, head brewer at the renascent Copper Dragon: "It's a bit like jazz. It's hard to explain what it is and what it isn't, but when you hear it, you know it's jazz."

This book explores Yorkshire's continuing contribution to this new jazz age.

Simon Jenkins, June 2019

Abbeydale Brewery

Unit 8, Aizlewood Road, Sheffield, S8 0YX; P: 0114 281 2712;
E: info@abbeydalebrewery.co.uk; W: abbeydalebrewery.co.uk;
F: @abbeydalebrewery; T: @abbeydalebeers.

South of Sheffield city centre, well away from the brewing heartland of the S3 postcodes, Yorkshire's first brewery alphabetically namechecks Beauchief Abbey which thrived here until the ravages of the dissolution. Kirkstall Brewery is another which preserves its ancient monastic name.

The brewery announced major expansion plans towards the end of 2018, annexing a neighbouring unit with more than £200,000 spent on new vessels, a malt milling system and laboratory equipment which would between them enable a 20% increase in capacity, and the potential for their own events space.

Abbeydale is now the city's biggest brewery and more than half of production is given over to the golden **Moonshine** (4.3%) – a bronze medallist at 2018's Champion Beer of Britain awards, while another regular is the amiably grapefruity **Deception** (4.1%), a former Sheffield Beer of the Year.

Serenity (3.8%) is a changing IPA where each batch focusses on a single hop. Past iterations included Azaaca and Galaxy, but the one I tried carried the significant pine and tropical fruit you would expect from Idaho 7. Abbeydale are big adopters of canning, and as we went to press they were starting to can the dangerously strong **Last Rites** (11%), a barley wine first brewed over 20 years ago.

The brewery's restless enthusiasm for experimentation is perhaps best illustrated by their ever-evolving Brewers Emporium range, covering all manner of styles, and by a recent Funk Festival celebrating sour and barrel-aged beers. For me, their raspberry macaroon white stout **Indulgence** (4.6%), was a curious missed step, its overwhelming impression being one of blue cheese, lovely with crackers, less so as a liquid. Their two pubs, the Rising Sun in Nether Green and Devonshire Cat in Sheffield city centre are perhaps the best places to sit in divine judgment.

🍺 **Heathen** (4.1%)

There is a moment, just as you prepare to take your first sip, just as your nose is filled with the wonderful heady zest of grapefruit and pineapple, that you wonder if you've picked up a can of Lilt by mistake. The liquid is the same enticing gold, both have colourful cans, and that big fruit blast just before the beer crosses the threshold has all the sunshine zing of the totally tropical taste.

And yet, as soon as it hits the palate, Heathen's hop character barges determinedly to the foreground, throwing its big bitter weight about. And though there's a little spike of carbonation, there's nothing here to match the full-on fizz of a fruity pop. Yet in the aftertaste, more of the citrus emerges in a dusty dry finish.

Heathen is styled an American pale ale, and the significant hopping is very much a trademark of the genre, though this one's moderate strength and ultimately quaffable character ensure that it remains wholly (and holy) in the mainstream.

Acorn Brewery

Unit 3 Aldham Industrial Estate, Wombwell, Barnsley, S73 8HA;
P: 01226 270734; W: acorn-brewery.co.uk; E: info@acorn-brewery.co.uk;
T: @acornbrewery

Dave and Judy Hughes used a redundant 10-barrel kit from a pub in the defunct Firkin chain to establish Acorn in 2003, and have since upgraded to a 25-barrel plant.

The brewery's one pub, the Old No 7 in the centre of Barnsley, is a four-time CAMRA regional pub of the year. Rich and rounded chestnut-coloured **Barnsley Bitter** (3.8%), with its long bitter finish, is perhaps their best-known product, having been Champion Beer of Britain Finalist on many occasions. Others include ultra-pale session ale **Yorkshire Pride** (3.7%), a permanent bottled beer on P&O cruise ship Britannia, liquorice-accented **Old Moor Porter** (4.4%) and an **IPA** (5%) which uses a different single hop every time.

Jet black, firmly bitter **Gorlovka** (6%) is named in honour of the Eastern Ukrainian city twinned with Barnsley – and is the Acorn take on the Imperial Stout style. It has a complex beefy taste that melds strong black coffee and dark chocolate and just a hint of coconut. A monthly-changing list of specials and seasonals complete the line-up; Barnsley beers are widely available in cask, keg and bottle.

 Acorn Blonde (4%)

When I held a beer tasting at Waterstone's in Leeds a while back, I began by introducing punters to this easy-drinking, crisp and refreshing pale ale – which is not a million miles from a continental lager. Acorn Blonde is very pale of colour and has a sweet, almost floral aroma, and some flowery citric notes persist into a sharp taste that buzzes around the palate with a significant amount of carbonation. The aftertaste is short-lived and faintly metallic – but as one of my Waterstone's tasters put it: "One brief encounter with this Barnsley Blonde wasn't nearly enough for me. Does anyone have her number?"

Ainsty Ales

Manor Farm, Acaster Malbis, YO23 2TY;
P: 01904 703233; W: ainstyales.co.uk;
E: info@ainstyales.co.uk; T/F: @ainstyales

Ainsty Ales could be the only brewhouse in Britain to have a piano in the corner, and though the daily variations of humidity and temperature have forced it well out of tune, it still gets played at their weekly Friday Night Socials.
Named after the 'York and Ainsty Wapentake', a medieval subdivision of the county, Ainsty finally put down roots in Acaster Malbis in 2016, having spent time cuckoo brewing with Brass Castle in Malton. Sharp and fruity pale ale **Angel** (3.6%) is a permanent, as is blonde **Flummoxed Farmer** (4%) their biggest-selling beer, along with best bitter **Bantam** (4.2%) and oatmeal stout **Assassin** (4.9%), both of which were SIBA award winners in 2018. Others include double gold winning American pale ale **Cool Citra** (4.4%) and low-alcohol pale **Ainsty Lite** (2.8%).

All Hallows Brewery

Main Street, Goodmanham, East Yorkshire, YO43 3JA; P: 01430 873849;
W: goodmanhamarms.co.uk; F: @goodmanhamarms; T: @VLogozzi

Decked in brasses, kettles and jugs, portraits and countryside scenes, polished wood and pewter mugs, the lovely red-brick Goodmanham Arms is almost the perfect country pub. Its food is fulsome and hearty, its welcome genuine and its choice of beers a little encyclopaedia of Yorkshire brewing. Both pub and the 11-gallon All Hallows brewery next door are run by Vito and Abbie Logozzi. Their flagship ale is the dark and sweetish mild **Peg Fyfe** (3.6%) whose name honours a 17th-century witch executed nearby. One of her victims was **Ragged Robyn** and there's sweet, biscuity, dark fruit notes and plenty of substance to the 4.7% deep maroon ale which takes his name. **Mischief Maker** (4%) is their traditional session ale; several other local pubs now serve All Hallows beers.

 No Notion (5.7%)
This big bodied porter, which lathers the palate with tobacco, red wine and chocolate, distils the sublime atmosphere of the Goodmanham Arms into a glass of micro-brewed beauty. Rich, soporific, comfortable as an old leather saddle, it's like dropping in briefly on a different kind of life.

Ampleforth Abbey Beer

Ampleforth, York, YO62 4EY; P: 01439 766811;
W: ampleforthabbeydrinks.org.uk; E: abbeydrinks@ampleforth.org.uk;
F: @ampleforthabbeydrinks; T: @ampleforthbeer

Fleeing France after the revolution, a community of Benedictine Monks founded Ampleforth Abbey in 1802, bringing with them the secret recipe for dark and full-bodied, spicy, biscuity Belgian Dubbel style **Ampleforth Abbey Beer** (7%). The monastic order continues to thrive, as does production of their single bottled beer, which has won a string of awards, including being named best drink in the 2012 Deliciously Yorkshire Award. The beer is now made at Little Valley Brewery; in recent times the monks have added a premium cider to their devotions.

Anthology Brewing - see p12

Asylum Harbour

7 Raincliffe Avenue, Scarborough, YO12 5BU; P: 07445 746511;
W: asylumharbour.co.uk; Email: info@asylumharbour.co.uk;
F: @asylumharbour; T: @asylumharbouruk

Raincliffe Avenue is an attractive street of bungalows, brick-built semis and sizeable detached homes, about a mile west of Scarborough's long sandy beaches. Hidden in a spacious garage is Asylum Harbour's brewery, established in 2014, which describes itself as "Not a microbrewery, not even a nano-brewery. Fifty litres per time and small through choice." Regular beers include a crisp **Pilsner** (5.5%), an **East Coast IPA** (6%) and a **Coriander Wheat Beer** (6.4%). But I'm most intrigued by the 10% **Rasputin Nut Oil** imperial stout, which I have yet to track down. Fat Cat in Sheffield and The Epicurean in Scarborough often provide a safe haven for beers from this unlikely suburban asylum.

🍺 Wheat Beer (5%)

When Hoegaarden first made inroads into the British market this was for many drinkers an alien experience. A cloudy yellow beer with suggestions of banana and cloves, it bore little relation to anything we had tried before, except perhaps on brave excursions into the brewpubs of northern Europe. A couple of decades on, wheat beers are now very much a staple of our own drinking culture; all decent bars offer at least one.

And though the Asylum Harbour version bears all the genre's essential characteristics, it is sufficiently subtle and gentle it might even win over the remaining doubters.

It pours a shimmering hazy gold – the instructions on the slender curvy bottle advise drinkers to swirl the dregs around the inside to allow the yeast into the taste – and it releases just a faint toffee aroma. On the palate there is a hint of cloves and ginger, and perhaps some of the sweetness of banana toffee, but the overall experience is a lovely, amiable introduction to the world of the wheat.

Anthology Brewing

Unit 6, Armley Link, Armley Road, Leeds, LS12 2QN;
P: 07594 975245;
W: anthologybrewing.co.uk;
E: info@anthologybrewing.co.uk;
F/T: @anthologybrewco

Former musician Liam Kane is the driving force behind this brand new one-man operation close to Armley jail. Drinkers' favourites like the Cardigan Arms, Whitelocks and Brudenell Social Club are early adopters of his ever-changing hop-forward pale ales such as the **New England Session Pale** (3.8%), **Dry Hopped Pale** (5%) and **US Session IPA** (4.5%). Special events at Liam's onsite taproom have begun to attract a significant following, too.

Atom Brewing

Unit 4, Food & Tech Park, Malmo Road, Hull, HU7 0YF; P: 01482 820572;
W: atombeers.com;
E: drinks@atombeers.com;
F/T: @atombeers

"We didn't set it up to make beer," says Scotsman Allan Rice, rather knocking me sideways with the opening gambit of a conversation in his office above the brewery on the northern fringes of Hull. "Primarily we saw it as an educational outreach facility."

Allan has a degree in physiology, his wife Sarah a PhD in biochemistry, and it's their passion for science which drives Atom, an enthusiasm evident both in the names of their beers and in the regular educational sessions they lay on for students from nearby schools and colleges.

Allan recognises something of himself in the young people of Hull: "It's quite similar to my home town of Greenock. We want to inspire this next generation to understand that science can be relevant to them. Coming here they can actually use their mathematics, their chemistry, their thermodynamics, and begin to think: 'I can do this.'" He cites the example of one student who lacked confidence at college, but after sessions at Atom, where he was given the chance to trust his own knowledge and make decisions about specific gravity and fermentation times, he began to thrive in class.

His long-term plan is to move to a new site where quadrupling brewing capacity will go hand in hand with plans to open a lecture theatre, laboratory and classroom. A further stage could be to establish a foundation, separate to the brewery, which would both support local charities and help young people to pursue their scientific ambitions.

Atom certainly do things a little differently – running beer schools for people to learn the process from start to finish, fronting up about brews which have gone wrong rather than pouring them quietly down a drain. They also have a city centre venue which enables them to get direct feedback on all their beers and gain a better understanding of what the consumer ultimately wants from their beer.

"Partnerships are also key for us," says Allan. "This year we will be working closely with the chemistry department at the University of Hull on a new novel technique to categorise beer and beer components to enable end-to-end statistical analysis which should greatly improve consistency."

He relishes the challenge of doing something difficult, a case in point being their full-bodied mini hop bomb **Schrodinger's Cat** (3.5%), which he admits is "a nightmare to produce", not least because it uses a novel mashing technique devised in conjunction with a Brazilian student. Characteristically, the very challenge of its brewing secures this a place on Atom's core list, alongside session IPA **Quantum State** (4.2%), **Pulsar Pilsner** (4.4%) and flagship American pale ale **Catalyst** (5.4%) which is big on juiciness and has a pleasing mouthfeel.

"We want to be consistent, but we still want to experiment," says Allan, explaining that of the 165 different brews tried so far, two thirds have now been retired. Yet it is that restless spirit of adventure which gives us the triple IPA **Mars** (11%), a quantity of which is being matured in old Rioja casks; and hop-free beers **Isotope** (10%) brewed with elderflower and bog myrtle and **Dark Alchemy** (4.9%) spiced with coriander and cardamom.

There's no fining, no filtering; "We just do it all by time," says Allan. "We do our analysis by sense."

With plans to open a second venue this year – and the opportunities afforded by a juicy contract with Asda – more and more drinkers are enjoying the magical chemistry of Atom.

BAD Co

Unit 3, North Hill Road, Dishforth Airfield, YO7 3DH; P: 01423 324 005;
W: wearebad.co; E: cheers@wearebad.co; F: @badcobrewinganddistilling;
T: @wearebadco

Having honed his skills during numerous visits to America's great craft breweries, Paul Holden-Ridgway established a microbrewery for his customers at the excellent Blind Jack's in Knaresborough, before establishing BAD Co in 2014. BAD stands for Brewing And Distilling, though I've yet to see any evidence that the craft brewer, based on Dishforth Airfield in North Yorkshire, has done any actual distilling as yet. If I were them, I wouldn't bother; the range of beers is impressive enough as it is. They include the amber, big bodied IPA **Wild Gravity** (5.2%) whose slightly sulphurous aroma is soon displaced by some hoppy, oily, resinous character, zipped around the palate by some significant carbonation.

Others confirm a love for classic rock: **Comfortably Numb** (3.8%) is a pale ale, **Love Over Gold** (4.1%) a hearty blonde, **Satisfaction** (6.7%) a sturdy brown ale aged in bourbon casks. Heavyweight quantities of aromatic hops make their presence felt in the tropical fruit blast of **Whiter Shade of Pale** (3.2%) which is tempered on the palate by malt and oatmeal that drag the beer from the IPA extremes to the drinkable pale ale mainstream.

Pillow Fight (4.8% ABV) is a curious beast – vanilla and marshmallow muffle the smoky nature of the roasted malts and Peruvian cacao, before some interesting damp woody notes take over in a distinctive finish. I'm sure Paul had fun putting it together, but it's almost as though he has done so much to achieve a compromise between its different elements, that it has ended up a whole heap of nothing much at all.

With its aroma of red wine and raisins, **Dark Necessities** (5.5%) is

Paul's milk stout, lactose adding a creamy richness to a brew packed with dark fruit, black coffee and a suggestion of vanilla.

Dazed and Confused (5.5%), jet black and beautiful with its chocolatey, cappuccino aromas, looks almost too good drink. The taste was never likely to quite match up to that visual promise, and yet it does pretty well, stroking the palate with silky waves of bitter dark chocolate, which recede into a strident smoky finish. The blonde, busty, beer-holding Britannia of the logo doesn't look like she would be bad company at all. "I wanted a woman, never bargained for you," as the song goes.

 ## Boston Tea Party (5.8%)

The original Boston Tea Party of 1773 was a protest against British colonial rule and in particular the Tea Act, which allowed the British East India Company to sell Chinese tea in America, without paying tax – giving them a significant commercial advantage. Now seen as a key moment in America's battle for independence, protesters boarded British ships and threw an entire consignment of tea into Boston harbour.

The beer which commemorates this event is inspired by the beers of New England, rather than anything produced by Typhoo. It has the kind of opaque haze which a decade ago would have had you staring in astonishment that something with this appearance had been deemed good enough to put into the public domain. Nowadays it's the sign of a brewery high on confidence and a public accustomed to beer unfiltered and unfined.

American Summit and Mosaic hops between them create a full-blooded tropical fruit flavour, with lime and lemon in the aroma and further grapefruit in the taste, where the German Magnum hop exerts its fabulous bitter influence. There's a dry, dusty finish – with perhaps just a suggestion of dark bitter chocolate – which has you reaching for more; a whole shipload ideally.

Bad Seed Brewery

7 Rye Close, York Road Business Park, Malton, YO17 6YD; P: 01653 695783;
W: badseedbrewery.com; E: info@badseedbrewery.com;
F/T: @badseedbrewery

The natural haze which hangs in a Bad Seed beer denotes a brewery which eschews fining and filtering to derive the fullest aroma, flavour and body from its bottled ales – most of which are vegan friendly. Bad Seed was established on an industrial estate in Malton by actor Chris Waplington who is now winning ripples of appreciative applause for his beer.

The curtain rises with the slight, inoffensive **Aussie Pale** (3.8%) and the story unfolds by way of the wheat, spice, bubblegum and banana of **Hefeweizen** (5.1%) and the surprisingly malty American Pale Ale **Cascade** (5.4%).

Bad Seed's minimalist pump clips are easy to spot, and a general guarantor of quality, interesting, unfined and unfiltered cask beer; their bottled beers are often found in specialist off licences.

The formidable cloudy amber **IPA** (7.3%) is an absolute beast of a beer – and perhaps requires a stage manager to step in front of the safety curtain and warn that this is not a production for the faint-hearted. The aroma's opening salvo of passion fruit is immediately supplanted by big juicy, piney hop resins which continue to dominate through the taste, before just a suggestion of sweetness emerges in a dramatic denouement. If you love your bitter hops, love that feeling of drinking something sumptuous, substantial, almost heavy, this could provide all the theatre you need.

 Espresso Stout (6.5%)

This one does everything you would expect of a beer so named, announcing itself with the big coffee aroma that hangs above a jet black ale with a foaming beige head. Silky smooth on the palate, the rich tastes of dark chocolate and bitter black coffee mingle with a dusty, slightly sour dryness, that melts away with some suggestions of toffee in the aftertaste.

Baytown Brewery

Station Road Stores, Station Road, Robin Hood's Bay, Whitby, YO22 4RA;
P: 01947 880202; W: baytownrhb.com; E: info@baytownrhb.com;
F: @baytownrhb; T: @smugglergeorge

Search the Baytown website for the story of the brewery and you'll find tales of contraband, hidden tunnels and secret recipes – and the ancient diary of a smuggler which revealed his scrapes with the customs men. Baytown was the 18th century locals' name for Robin Hood's Bay, and the website makes great play of the fact that the village's dramatic location amid the North Yorkshire cliffs may once have been the setting for this most ancient of criminal professions.

And there's some quality ale behind the hype. Pale and malty **Press Gang's Arrival** (3.8%) is their entry-level easy-drinking ale while the full-bodied **Smuggler's Haul** (6%) concentrates these flavours into a simple, bold, strong bitter. **Squire's Connivance** (5%) is a dark porter packed with chocolate, liquorice and aniseed, while the ruby ale **Whitby Heritage** (4.4%) features the work of famous local Victorian photographer Frank Meadow Sutcliffe on an eye-catching pump clip. Several of the Baytown beers are also available in bottle – and are served on the Newcastle-Amsterdam ferry too – but sampling these beers while drinking in the spectacular panoramic views of the resort's Victoria Hotel is probably the perfect Baytown experience.

Baytown Bitter (4%)

The slightly sweet, butterscotchy ale pours an attractive pale golden brown, topped with an extravagant foaming head. While there's no significant aroma, once on the palate it charges around like a cutlass-wielding pirate, showing off its full-bodied malty weight. Only in the finish does the balance tip towards the bitterness of the hops, just as it should in a traditional, sessionable Yorkshire bitter.

Beer Ink

Plover Road Garage, Plover Road, Lindley, Huddersfield, HD3 3PJ;
P: 01484 643368; W: beer-ink.co.uk; E: Sales@beer-ink.co.uk;
F: @BeerInk.ltd; T: @BeerInkBrewCo

This former garage site was first taken on as a brewery by Mallinsons in 2008, and also hosted the now-defunct Hand Drawn Monkey, before Beer Ink began production here in 2016 – since when brewer Ryan Stoppard has created more than 60 different brews. They are enjoyed in the on-site taproom and quality alehouses such as The Shakespeare in Sheffield, Foley's in Leeds and Grove in Huddersfield. Ryan is also on the look-out for potential brewery tap premises in Lindley.

Beer Ink's draught beer range includes other regulars **Pin-Up** pale ale (4%), **Noire** stout (5%) and **Two Faced** DIPA (7.5%). **Avant Garde** (4%) is styled as a non-traditional bitter, and despite its moderate strength delivers sufficient taste and character to edge it adrift of the sessionable end of the traditional bitter market. There is some enticing toffee in the aroma of a beer which pours a deep hazy brown with a bright foaming head and amid its oily texture is a taste of caramel and dried fruit, the

product of a cocktail of hops from three continents in the brew.

Seasonal beers allow Ryan to stretch himself with some imaginative recipes such as the peanut butter stout **Starbeer** (8.5%), the range of fruit sours in his **Berry Superstitious** range (4.2%), and the peach and pink peppercorn saison **Peppa Peach** (4.9%). And in the sociable world of modern brewing, Ryan has further indulged his passion for great new beer through collaborations with some of the best in the business – Wilde Child, Abbeydale and Brewdog among them.

🍺 **Red Weizen Blue** (5.1%)

The explosion in brewing over the past couple of decades has obliged breweries to create really eye-catching names and labels in order to allow their products to really stand out from the competition – whether that's on the bar top or the supermarket shelves. So full marks to Beer Ink for the ingeniously-titled Red Weizen Blue, a German-style wheat beer inspired by the American craft beer scene. The double-headed eagle with wings emblazoned in the flags of the two countries emphasises the cultures which have come together to create this new beer.

Red Weizen Blue bears some wheat beer hallmarks – a pale cloudy gold ale beneath a foaming white head – but the American hop-happy influence shows through in a really dry and bitter taste, which is all zipped around by some significant carbonation.

Beer Monkey Brew Co.

*Enterprise Way, Airedale Business Centre,
Skipton, BD23 2TZ; P: 01756 701289;
W: beermonkeybrewco.com;
E: info@beermonkeybrewco.com;
T: @BeerMonkeybrew_*

By buying up their equipment, saving their
staff from redundancy and moving into their
Skipton premises in 2017, Beer Monkey
stepped into the void left by the demise of
Copper Dragon – though that famous
Yorkshire brewery has now been revived in
nearby Keighley. The range is focussed on
four permanent cask and bottled ales: the
bright and effervescent **Blonde** (3.8%),
crisp and award-winning **Evolution Pilsner**
(4.3%), the traditional English ale **Bitter
Revival** (3.9%) and **Uncle Monk's IPA** (see
below). Seasonal ales fill out the range of a
brewery whose products are gradually
reaching bars and pubs across the north.

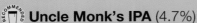 **Uncle Monk's IPA** (4.7%)

Bright and golden Uncle Monk's is a
traditional India Pale Ale with a light floral
aroma and a foaming head which retains its
shape as it falls. The taste has a significant
deep dryness with the bitterness of hop
resins rather than the overt juicy fruitiness
you would expect from a new-wave
American IPA. Neither is it as strong as
some, simply an easy-going sessionable
pale ale cut from the same cloth as those
amiable Copper Dragon brands.

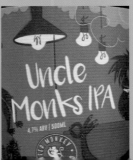

Beespoke Brewery

The Fox, 41 Briggate, Shipley, BD17 7BP; F: @beespokebrewery

The addition of a one-barrel brewing plant in the cellars brought a new dimension to The Fox, an excellent micropub just outside the centre of Shipley. The standout ale is the sleepy, silky, delicate **Shipley Stout** (4.6%), while others include the firm and bitter **Beeboppalula** (4.2%) and the full-bodied **Crowthers Blackpowder Porter** (5.4%).

Bilbrough Top Brewery

St James House, Main Street, Bilbrough, YO23 3PH; P: 07767 333555; W: https://btb.beer; E: nigelcay@gmail.com; F/T: @bilbroughtop

Motoring enthusiast Nigel Cay named this new brewery to honour both the village and *Top Gear*, though the only one I have so far caught up with is an easy-going **Blonde** (3.9%). I'm sure Mr Clarkson would approve.

Bingley Brewery

2, Old Mill Yard, Shay Lane, Wilsden, Bradford BD15 0DR; P: 01535 274285; W: bingleybrewery.co.uk; E: info@bingleybrewery.co.uk; F: @bingleybrewery.co.uk; T: @BingleyBrewery

Owner and brewer Darren Marks established Bingley Brewery in 2014 and has built a strong local reputation around products such as toffee and citrus blonde ale **Goldy Locks** (4%), roasted malt and liquorice stout **1848** (4.8%) and spicy, berry-bearing red ale **Blantyre** (5%). Drinkers who love their hop-front American-influenced pales will find the juicy, piny, slightly spicy **Jamestown** (5.4%) well worth a visit.

Recent additions include the smooth and spicy porter **Lock Keeper** (5.7%), the double dry hopped North **South Divide** (5.6%) and the silky chocolatey **Moo Moo** (4.9%) which is given a beautiful sweet edge by Madagascan vanilla.

Bingley bottled beers are available to buy at the brewery and at locally selected stockists. Their onsite brewery bar does a healthy trade, opening on the first Friday of every month.

Black Sheep Brewery

Wellgarth, Crosshills, Masham, HG4 4EN; P: 01765 689227;
W: blacksheepbrewery.com; E: reception@blacksheep.co.uk;
F: @blacksheepbrewery; T: @blacksheepbeer

The story of how separate branches of the Theakston family came to own Masham's two rival brewers has been so oft-told it hardly bears further repetition. Both trace a bloodline to Robert Theakston, who turned his back on the family's cattle farm to lease the town's Black Bull brewhouse in 1827. Theakston's retain his name, Black Sheep prize their 'first son' provenance.

Townsfolk tend to take sides. Most have a connection to one or other brewery, and choose their pint accordingly. "Masham folk tend to drink either Theakston Best or Black Sheep Bitter," one local tells me. The stronger beers – Old Peculier and Riggwelter – are "mostly for the tourists."

Of which there are plenty. Around 50,000 call in at the Black Sheep visitor centre every year, many joining the hour-long tour which winds through the site before ending at the attractive Bistro and Baaa'r (geddit), where a proud line of handpumps dispenses their cask range: dry, peppery, sessionable **Best Bitter** (3.8%), full bodied **Black Sheep Special Ale** (4.4%), big-tasting fruit-cakey **Riggwelter** (5.9%) and New World pale **Baa Baa** (4%).

Each is brewed in traditional Yorkshire Square vessels – actually they are stainless steel and circular, but the process is precisely the same as when they were four-cornered and made of slate. Creamy amber-coloured **Yorkshire Square Ale** (5%) with its placid malty aroma, fulsome, bitter taste and suggestions of dried fruit, almonds and orange marmalade, celebrates this distinct style.

A restless spirit for experimentation has seen a host of new beers added to the roster in recent times. Iridescent golden **Venus and**

Rob and Jo Theakston

Mars (4.5%) draws the sizzle of zesty orange, pine and stone fruit from its cocktail of First Gold, Summit and Chinook hops; jet black **Choc Orange Stout** (6.1%) brings to the palate the complexity of cigar smoke, black coffee, chilli and lime, to add to the Terry's Chocolate Orange of the aroma. With its fearsome image of a horned white beast with eyebrows to rival the Gallagher brothers, **Glug M'Glug** (6.2%) is said to recall a mythical creature which once roamed the Yorkshire hills. This dark IPA lingers as a deep red brown in the glass, with a foaming ivory head, hitting the palate with the firm bitterness you would associate with a typical pale IPA, before delivering sufficient backbone of rich malt and toffee to remind you of its strength.

The brewery is a strong supporter of the Tour de Yorkshire. Light and easy-going **Velo** (4.2%) celebrates the relationship with a tangy, spicy, effervescent freewheel downhill in the summer sunshine. The warming pale ale **Pathmaker** (5.6%) honours the remarkable life and work of brewery founder Paul Theakston, who – more than 25 years on – remains company chairman, though the day-to-day running of the brewery has passed to sons Rob and Jo.

🍺 **Imperial Russian Stout** (8.5%)

Strong dark meaty porters were exported from London to the Baltic states from the late 18th century – and gained their Imperial title due to the enthusiastic patronage of that lady of prodigious appetites, Czarina Catherine the Great. By the outbreak of the First World War – and certainly by the time of the Russian Revolution three years later – this once lucrative trade route had all but dried up. For decades the only British brewery retaining the name was John Smith's. It was this Tadcaster beer which ultimately sparked the revival of the style, its export to America re-awakening interest in these dark and seriously potent beers.

And just as many brewers have created all manner of India Pale Ales, so have several re-visited this genre too.

Holding the Black Sheep version to the light reveals its attractive deep red browns, while the aroma is a sensuous bouquet of red wine, cigar smoke and decadent, narcotic Turkish coffee – like you've fast-forwarded to the last knockings of an elaborate dinner in a secretive salon in the back streets of Paris or Casablanca or Istanbul. From here the sweetness of black treacle and caramel floods the palate, as this beer of distinctive flavour works its mysterious soporific magic.

Only in the long and significant, luxurious smoky aftertaste does some tartness of blackcurrant develop to give the suggestion of a sharper edge.

Blue Bee Brewery

Unit 29-30, Hoyland Road Industrial Estate, Sheffield, S3 8AB;
P: 07375 659349; W: bluebeebrewery.co.uk;
E: sales@bluebeebrewery.co.uk; F/T:@bluebeebrewery

Hefty, flag-waving quantities of mosaic, citra and equinox hops created the patriotic bugle blast of citrus and tropical fruit in Blue Bee's **Born in the USA** (6%) which was Champion at Huddersfield Beer Festival in 2016. Now just an occasional, this wonderful example of a new age IPA complements the brewery's regular range which includes summery, floral

Reet Pale (4%), traditional bronze-coloured bitter **Hillfoot Best** (4%) and full-bodied but still easy-going coffee-ish **Tempest Stout** (4.8%). As it heads towards its tenth anniversary next year, this ten-barrel cask-only brewery's relentlessly adventurous spirit spawns an ever-changing list of specials, seasonals, collaborations and occasionals. A close relationship to the famous Kelham Island Tavern provides a ready route to market.

Bone Machine

Taphouse Brewpub, 70 Humber St, Hull, HU1 1TU; P: 01482 618000;
E: beer@bonemachinebrewing.com; F: @bonemachinebrewco;
T: @bonemachinebrew

Launched early in 2019, the Taphouse on Hull's resurgent waterfront is the new home for Finnish brothers Marko and Kimi Karjalainen who launched Bone Machine in Pocklington two years earlier and now distribute their distinctive brews across the UK and to outlets in Finland, Sweden and the Netherlands.

Hazy yellow **Garden Of Death** (7%) is an in-your-face New England IPA with a blast of musty fruit zests in the aroma and a taste dominated by pineapple with a not-unpleasant undercurrent of stewing vegetables. The powerful stout **Mary Ann Is Dead** (7.4%) has the chocolate notes you often find with these strong dark roasty ales – but here the brothers blend it with mint to create an engaging flavour often explored in ice cream and after-dinner sweets, but rarely in beer. Several others in the range reference mortality in the name, but not all.

The brothers share the new brewery with Yorkshire Brewing Company (see page 200) and between them they will produce beers from across the range from the fiercely traditional to the experimental and contemporary and extend Bone Machine's penchant for collaboration.

Bosun's Brewery

Unit 4, Prospect Business Centre, Prospect St, Huddersfield, HD1 2NU;
P: 01484 412300; W: bosunsbrewery.co.uk; E: sales@bosunsbrewery.co.uk;
F: @bosunsbrewingcompany; T: @bosunsbrewery

The beautifully-designed, naval-themed pump clips of Bosun's Brewery promise a safe haven for any storm-tossed drinker – and reflect brewer Grahame Andrews' previous career at sea. The no-nonsense earthy, full-bodied brown ale **Maiden Voyage** (3.9%) was the first Bosun's beer to be released, and remains a local favourite, and I have a real soft spot for the full-bodied, deeply citric **King Neptune** (4.3%). Among a changing list of seasonals, beers worth pursuing across the oceans include the lemony, peachy golden **Bermuda Triangle** (4.1%), the substantially bitter **Golden Rivet** (3.7%) and the sweetly dangerous **Pirate Mocha Stout** (4.3%).

Having been established in Wakefield in 2012, the brewery has recently sailed west to Huddersfield, where plans to hoist the brewery flag over an onsite bar are well advanced as we go to press.

Horbury Blonde

Against all this seafaring malarkey, the 3.9% Horbury Blonde seems a curious name, the Wakefield suburb being somewhat landlocked. But its attractive bright golden colour, its yeasty, bready aroma and its malty, wheaty nature, sharpened by some strident juicy fruit hop character in the later throes of the taste, ought to appeal to mariner and landlubber alike.

Bradfield Brewery

Watt House Farm, High Bradfield, Sheffield, S6 6LG; P: 0114 2851118;
W: bradfieldbrewery.com; E: info@bradfieldbrewery.com;
F:@bradfieldbrewery; T: @BradfieldBrew

Watt House was a working Peak District dairy farm before its diversification into brewing; they went from milking 100 cows a week to brewing 100,000 pints of ale a week, using pure millstone grit springwater. The first pint was served in 2005 at The Nags Head in Loxley; this and the King and Miller in Deepcar are now the two brewery taps. Their award-winning ultra-pale **Blonde** (4%) with its marked citrus and summer fruit aromas is their entry-level product, with other permanents including oat-fortified **Stout** (4.5%), and big-selling winter ale, **Belgian Blue** (4.9%), while a good list of seasonals completes the catalogue. The brewery is a big sponsor of Sheffield's phenomenally successful ice-hockey side the Steelers.

 ### Bradfield Farmer's Pale Ale (5%)

Some fresh, floral notes emerge from the foaming white head of the aroma of this dry and fruity beer. On the palate its quiet toffee flavours are neatly balanced by some determined hoppy bitterness, the tastes zipped around by some zingy, prickly carbonation.

Brass Castle Brewery

10A Yorkersgate, Malton, YO17 7AB; P: 01653 698683;
W: brasscastle.co.uk; E: online@brasscastlebrewery.co.uk;
F: @brasscastlebrewery; T: @brasscastlebeer

Though the brewery has long since relocated from Phil Saltonstall's one-barrel plant in his garage, Brass Castle Hill in Pocklington is now immortalised by his quality craft beers which have gained a following both in Yorkshire and overseas.

The core range includes malt-forward classics **Northern Blonde** (3.9%) and **Helles Lager** (4.4%), which is based on the light Munich lager style. Vanilla porter **Bad Kitty** (5.5%) was the second beer Phil ever brewed, and remains the brewery's best-known beer and comes available in many formats, including wood barrel-aged, rum and Christmas-spiced variants.

Misfit (4.3%) is a rotating hop-swap beer, featuring regularly changing hop combinations, **Sunshine** (5.7%) celebrates the classic IPA style while **Disruptor** (7.4%) is a temperate juicy rendition of the modern New England-style IPA.

The Brewery Taphouse is open Tuesday through Sunday and offers cosy comfort amid reclaimed wood and barrels; a Crowler machine allows drinkers to take away just under a litre of their favourite beer in a sealed can filled at the bar.

To fully exercise their new canning line, this year Brass Castle initiated a 'Bigger Picture' treasure hunt series of canned beers which has had drinkers scrabbling around the Yorkshire countryside mapping the county's myths and legends in a search for buried treasure.

Hoptical Illusion (4.3%)

All Brass Castle beers are vegan and vegetarian friendly – but this one is also gluten-free. Animal-derived products aren't allowed near the brewhouse, and a commitment to ecology extends to spent hops enriching the produce of local allotments and spent grain being used to create biogas and fertiliser. Hoptical Illusion is the gluten-free version of their single hopped Comet pale ale. It pours a dull, slightly cloudy pale gold, and has a beautiful rich, dry, bitterness to the taste, no doubt the product of the hops, but not overly fruity or piney – and with absolutely bags of taste for a beer of its moderate strength. It even delivers a little warming glow in the finish.

Breworks

The Black Swan, 18 Birdgate, Pickering, YO18 7AL; P: 01751 242401;
W: blackswan-pickering.co.uk/breworks; E: tris@breworks.co.uk

When brewer Tristan Hall began producing beer in
the Black Swan's old wash house, he revived a
tradition which stretches back at least to Victorian
times, though the last brewery here closed before
the First World War. Though Tristan's beers reach
pubs around the area, the Black Swan remains the
best place to try the range. Cask ales include the
light and golden, fruity, buttery **Istanbul Pale Ale**
(4.3%) and the bready, caramelly **Great Scot**
(3.9%), which marked a visit by the Flying
Scotsman to the North Yorkshire Moors Railway.

 Coal Porter (4.9%)
This substantial, cocoa-endowed, and beautifully-
named porter pulls across the tongue a
comfortable eiderdown of red wine, dark chocolate
and liquorice. Fabulous.

Brew Foundation

18 Jarrow Road, Sheffield, S11 8YB; P: 0114 282 3098;
W: thebrewfoundation.co.uk; E: sales@thebrewfoundation.co.uk;
T/F: @brewfoundation

Though firmly anchored to Sheffield, Brew Foundation's beers are
brewed at Wincle Brewery in Cheshire. Apparently 'Citra' hops are
referenced in **C-Bomb** (4.2%), which is a more delicate floral IPA than
the provocative name might suggest. The fabulously named **Janet's
Treat Porter** (4.8%) is a lovely fruit and chocolate concoction. For me
the white IPA **Wheat Your Heart Out** (6%) was an unedifying battle of
sweet and sour, but this is a brewery whose foundation is in
experimentation, so they can be excused a missed step from time to
time.

The brewery website lists a further ten beers in the roster and a tap
takeover during Sheffield's fantastic beer week in March 2019 allowed
customers at The York pub to compare and contrast.

Brew York

Unit 6, Enterprise Complex, Walmgate, York, YO1 9TT; P: 01904 848448;
W: brewyork.co.uk; E: sales@brewyork.co.uk; F/T: @brewyorkbeer

Brew York burst spectacularly onto the local scene in 2016, shrugging off the significant setback of metre-deep flooding to their riverside premises just three weeks after signing the lease. The ten-barrel craft brewery sits alongside a taproom where you can watch the brewers at work, and an impressive beer hall which serves quality street food and boasts the widest selection of beers in the city.

With its luscious, lustrous, sweet black darkness, the coconut, tonka bean, vanilla and cacao milk stout **Tonkoko** (4.3%) earned the brewery some early fame, with first prize at the city's beer festival. This and its bigger, harder cousin **Imperial Tonkoko** (7.5%) remain in the core range alongside American pale ale **Galaga** (4.7%) with its punchy tropical fruits, sour **Goose Willis** (5.3%) and vegan pale ales **X-Panda** (4.5%) and **JARSA** (3.7%).

A stunning beer garden looks out from the taproom across the water to the impressive Rowntree Wharf; thankfully flood protection measures guard against any future swelling of the Foss.

🍺 Little Eagle (4.5%)

In a world where the market for India Pale Ales is seemingly dominated by a race towards ever-more-heroic levels of bitterness, it is refreshing, literally so, to come across a beer which can genuinely be described as a session IPA. It's dry and really refreshing, but doesn't challenge the palate with the overt hop character of some IPAs. Instead it's a docile, easy-going ale which I could drink all night. And the calico jungle of the can's design is something rather wonderful, too.

Bricknell Brewery

Bricknell Avenue, Hull, HU5 4ET; W: bricknellbrewery.co.uk;
E: Richard@bricknellbrewery.co.uk; T: @BricknellBeers

Tiny Bricknell is the very essence of a one-man band. It was established by former Hull University lecturer Richard English who sold his sports car to set up the brewery in his garage in 2015 – and he does everything from the brewing, bottling, label sticking and delivery himself.

With a typical brew size of just 160 litres, Richard specialises in the production of unusual hand-crafted bottle-conditioned beers for just a handful of local bars and restaurants, though an occasional cask makes its way into the on-trade and to local beer festivals.

His range starts with straw-coloured **Saazy Blonde** (4%) a crisp and fresh tasting real ale targeted at the lager drinkers. **Cascade Pale** (4.4%) is an American-style pale ale, brewed with lashings of Cascade hops which exert an energetic grapefruit influence on the aroma and flavour.

Richard's stronger ales include malty, slightly sweet, dark ruby ale **Bosphorous 1875** (6%), based on a Victorian recipe, and the luxuriously treacly Imperial Russian Stout **Slavanka 1873** (7%), named after a ship built in Hull for the Russian Tsars. For those who like drinking at the extremes, Richard's Belgian-style **Meaux Abbey Ale** (9%) uses pale malts and an assortment of brown sugars to produce a strong, light ale with a complex gamut of flavours. New porters **Paragon** (5.8%) and **Stepney** (6.6%) namecheck Hull railway stations, though the latter went out with Beeching.

Without the considerable overheads which burden some other brewers of similar size, this remains a profitable trade: "I really do it because I love it," says Richard. "It's just an extension of my hobby."

###

Double Anchor IPA (6%)

Both this and its gentler cousin **Anchor Pale** (4.4%) are essentially traditional ales using English hops – in this case Goldings and Target, which you might have felt were rather out of fashion in the rush for all things American, particularly for any beer badged as an IPA. Double Anchor is far closer than many modern interpretations to what this genre originally stood for. A slightly cloudy amber, it lets loose some sweetish syrupy aromas, but these are soon overwhelmed by tastes of caramel, some woody notes and a long bitter aftertaste. Flaked oats add a lovely weighty substance to the whole experience.

Bridgehouse Brewery

Airedale Heifer, Bradford Road, Sandbeds, Keighley, BD20 5LY;
P: 01535 601222; W: bridgehousebrewery.co.uk;
E: info@bridgehousebrewery.co.uk

The presence of some Latin placeholder text "Lorem ipsum dolor…" on the Bridgehouse website suggests that this is an operation more concerned with creating great beer than polishing its customer relations front. The Airedale Heifer is its fourth location in less than a decade: Bridgehouse began life in Keighley using kit salvaged from Sowerby Bridge's defunct Ryburn Brewery and soon moved to Oxenhope, before merging with Old Bear at their Keighley site. A purpose-built brewery at the popular foody pub has at last found Bridgehouse a permanent home. Smooth ruby ale **Bridgehouse Porter** (4.5%) is packed with toffee and malt flavours; golden **Holy Cow** (5.6%) has theatrical levels of juicy, fruity hop flavour.

Bridlington Brewing Co

The Pack Horse, Market Place, Bridlington, YO16 4QJ; P: 01262 674592

Local real ale favourite the Pack Horse is the ideal place to try beers from this microbrewery, which was established in the nearby Telegraph Inn's beer garden in 2014 and moved to the Pack Horse in 2017. A recent flurry of appropriately equine-themed beers have included **Wonky Donkey** (4%), **Copper Horse** (4%) and **Farrier's Choice** (4%).

Briggs Signature Ales

Unit 1, Waterhouse Mill, 65-71 Lockwood Road, Huddersfield, HD1 3QU;
P: 07427 668004; W: briggssignatureales.weebly.com;
E: info@briggsales.co.uk; F: @briggsales; T: @briggssigales

Carpenter Nick Briggs developed a love of real ale while working in the building trade. After a spell working for Mallinsons, Nick struck out on his own, producing his own music-themed ales on the Huddersfield plant. They include piney, red-berry flavoured **Techno** (4.2%), the American-hop influenced **Northern Soul** (5.7%) and tropical fruit golden ale **Hip Hop** (4.2%). **Mash Up** (3.9%) typifies Yorkshire's "make do and mend" spirit by using hops left over from previous brews, while talented artist Martin Simpson provides Nick with the grotesques and ne'er-do-wells who feature on the pump clips.

Brown Cow Brewery

Brown Cow Road, Barlow, Selby, North Yorkshire, YO8 8EH; P: 01757 618947;
W: browncowbrewery.co.uk; E: susansimpson@browncowbrewery.co.uk

Almost 20 years of brewing earned Sue Simpson a prestigious award from Doncaster CAMRA in 2016 for exceptional services to real ale; she and partner Keith have established a solid reputation for their six-barrel plant from where they deliver cask beers within a 15-mile radius. Lager malt and American Cascade hops create the straw-pale **Sessions** (3.6%) which delivers some surprising citrus in the aftertaste while pale **White Dragon** (4%) offers a clean sharpness.

But it is their darker beers, the fulsome, slightly sweet **Thriller in Vanilla Porter** (5.1%) and the coffee-ish dark mild **Captain Oates** (4.5%) – named after Yorkshire's own hero of Antarctica – which have won a string of beer festival awards.

Butcher's Dog Brewery

Unit Four, Twydale Business Park, Skerne Road, Driffield, YO25 6JX;
P: 01377 254032; W: thebutchersdog.co.uk; E: info@thebutchersdog.co.uk;
F: @thebutchersdogdriffield

When former RAF technician Tim Waudby decided to turn his home brewing into a business, partner Nat's popular Driffield micropub the Brewer's Dog gave him a ready outlet for his produce.

Black treacle gives extra substance to deep red **Peppa's Pawter** (4.7%) – named after the couple's Dalmatian who also features on the pub logo. Cascade and Galaxy hops lend their citrus character to **Kukur IPA** (5.8%) while seven malts combine in the dry **Black Spot Stout** (4.6%).

A recent visit to the bar discovered none of these on sale, as the expectant mum had brought a pregnant pause to proceedings.

Burley Street Brewhouse

9 Burley Street, Leeds, LS3 1LD; P: 07506 741039;
W: www.burleystreetbrewhouse.co.uk; E: dawn@zigzaglighting.co.uk

A number of local brewers have taken the first steps towards business independence amid the tangle of pipework, wiring and hoses in the claustrophobic cellars of the Fox and Newt just outside Leeds city centre. The one-bedroomed Rutland Hotel operated here from Victorian times and after a gas explosion wrecked the neighbouring shop it re-opened as the Fox and Newt, having expanded across the blast site. The pub's front window and floorboards had to be removed for the brewkit to be installed in the 1980s; removing, replacing or even updating the kit is completely impossible without similar upheaval.

Over the years, a string of licensees have devoted varying levels of enthusiasm to the project. Its re-establishment as Burley Street Brewery in 2010 brought fresh continuity and the two regular beers have a healthy following in the pub upstairs and in its nearby sister pub the Pack Horse. They are blonde **Laguna Seca** (4%) whose tame sweetness is followed by the grapefruity dryness of Chinook and First Gold hops, and the well-balanced copper coloured best bitter **Brickyard** (3.8%).

Cap House Brewery

444 Victoria Works, Bradford Road, Batley, WF17 5LW;
P: 01924 479909; W: www.caphousebrewery.co.uk

Gary and Karen Wardman run the Reindeer Inn in Overton, which is the brewery tap for the beers produced by Gary and partner Peter Lister on a factory complex in nearby Batley. Cap House Colliery, now the National Mining Museum, is close to the Reindeer, and several beers draw on this proud subterranean heritage. You can certainly imagine sooted, work-weary colliers slaking their thirst on pints of the tangy, toffee-ish **Miners A Pint** (3.8%), or the brighter, sharper **Miner's Light** (4.2%) probably as close to a lager as any self-respecting Yorkshire pitman would ever dare venture. New Zealand's Nelson Sauvin hop lends white wine fruitiness to **Nelson IPA** (4.2%), while **North Pole** (4%), with its big blast of fresh orange, lemon and passion fruit, is one of a host of hearty Cap House blondes.

Captain Cook Brewery

White Swan, 1 West End, Stokesley, TS9 5BL; P: 01642 710263

Named after the famed local explorer, this brewery in the northern tip of the county was established in 1999 in the 18th century White Swan pub, which remains the best place to sample the wares – though their cask and bottled beers are sometimes more widely available.

Cathead Brewery

The Lion and Key, 48 High Street, Hull, HU1 1QE; P: 01482 225212

Irish-themed pub Durty Nelly's was a famous fixture on the Hull drinking circuit for years. It has now reverted to its original name and sources beer from the neighbouring Cathead brewery. The aromatic **Peach Tree Blonde** (4%) is evidence of some significant alchemy at work here.

Chantry Brewery

*Units 1-2 Callum Court, Gateway Industrial Estate, Parkgate,
Rotherham, S62 6NR; P: 01709 711866; W: chantrybrewery.co.uk;
E: sean@chantrybrewery.co.uk; F: @chantrybreweryrotherham;
T: @chantrybrewery*

Chantry Brewery is the only brewery remaining in a town whose brewing history stretches back through companies like Bentley's and Mappin's who competed for custom among those who laboured in Rotherham's furnaces and glass factories. Fittingly, Sheffield steel was used to create this 20-barrel plant, from whence comes the fresh, light **Steelos** (4.1%) with its subtle aromas of sweet orange, apricots and blackcurrants; well-balanced pine and blackberry **Full Moon** (4.2%) and the full-bodied stout **Diamond Black** (4.5%). Oily, toasty, **Special Reserve** (6.3%) is an old ale packed with black treacle, raisins and suggestions of red wine.

Bright, crisp and refreshing **New York Pale** (3.9%) honours a local factory which once furnished the Big Apple with its distinctive red fire hydrants. It was crowned Champion Bitter of Yorkshire at the 2018 Rotherham Real Ale Music Festival, where the firm porter **Two Magpies** (4.5%) was named best porter. The brewery has recently taken on the Cross Keys pub in Handsworth, while the famous old Cutlers Arms, a short walk from Rotherham's football stadium, is an appropriately-named venue to try the whole Chantry range.

🍺 Iron and Steel (4%)

With this name, this simple, sessionable copper-coloured bitter could only have been forged in the industrial heartland of South Yorkshire. Several breweries which have emerged in and around Sheffield in recent years celebrate this proud heritage – there's golden Brightshine Ale from Sheffield Brewery, Stancill's Stainless and Toolmakers Brewery's Lynchpin. Though Iron and Steel is only brewed to a modest strength, it is possessed of sufficient toffee character and an iron-like firmness to be suggestive of something rather stronger.

Chin Chin Brewing

Unit 53F, Langthwaite Business Park, South Kirkby, Pontefract, WF9 3NS; P: 07896 253650; E: andrew@chinchinbrewing.co.uk; F: @chinchinbrewing; T: @chinchinbrewing

The malty, sessionable amber ale **Little Boy Lost** (4.6%) is the only beer I've so far tracked down from this newcomer, though the Soldiers in South Elmsall and Fat Cat in Sheffield are among pubs which often sell their wares. Imminent plans to start bottling should hopefully make Chin Chin more widely available.

Cobbydale Brewery

47 Kirkgate, Silsden, BD20 0AQ; P: 01535 930884; E: lreids@gmail.com

The Cobbydale brewhouse is in the rear of the Red Lion pub in Silsden, which remains the best place to try the beers. They include firm and fruity **Eye Pee Aye** (6.1%), creamy stout **Dark Stuff** (5%) and their original premium bitter **Cobbyd Ale** (4.8%).

Cold Bath Brewing Co.

46 King's Road, Harrogate, HG1 5JW; T: 0330 880 7009; W: coldbathbrewing.com; E: info@coldbathbrewing.com

Established in 2018, a craft ale bar in the heart of Harrogate is home to this new microbrewery, where local legend Sean Franklin, once the driving force behind Rooster's, is now the master brewer. Efforts were initially concentrated on a single pale, crisp, floral and effervescent **Session Lager** (4.2%), but Cold Bath have diversified into an evolving range of small-batch ales and lagers which are already finding their way into an impressive range of bars, restaurants and off-licences, both across Yorkshire and further afield.

Concertina Brewery

Dolcliffe Rd, Mexborough, S64 9AZ; P: 01709 580841

300 Great Beers to Try Before You Die is a best-selling bucket-list book by world-renowned beer writer Roger Protz; the third beer featured is from the tiny brewery below this private members' club. **Bengal Tiger** (4.6%) is a revelatory India Pale Ale, a traditional cask ale packed with the kind of extravagant fruity, spicy, resinous hoppy flavours so sought after by the new wave crafties. The club itself – known locally as the Tina – dates back to the time when Mexborough's Concertina Band won prestigious prizes and played for Royalty. It is the only members' club in the UK which brews on the premises; thankfully non-members are also made welcome.

Cooper Hill Brewery

Unit 4 Highcliffe Mills, Bruntcliffe Lane, Morley, LS27 9LR;
P: 0113 307 4585; E: sales@barmaster.co; F: @cooperhillbrewery

Trinity Brewery, established in a disused toilet block of Wakefield's rugby league stadium, was one of the remarkable stories of this book's first edition. Now renamed, relocated and replenished with new fermenters and conditioning tanks, the brewery's story continues through a small range of cask ales which include the light, sessionable **Blonde** (3.8%) and the buttery, malty **Best** (3.8%).

Copper Dragon

Lee Mills, St Pauls Rd, Keighley, BD21 4QW; P: 01756 243243;
W: copperdragon.co.uk; E: steve@copperdragon.co.uk;
F: @copperdragonbrewery; T: @news_copper

"We grew too fast," admits boss Steve Taylor, looking back on how Copper Dragon exploded onto the scene in the first decade of the millennium, its breathtaking rise powered by the soaraway success of a single blonde ale, **Golden Pippin**. At first the brewery rode the crest of this considerable wave, before sliding into financial difficulties. This tale might have remained just a cautionary note to others, but for the Taylor family's determination to remain in the industry – and their indignation at others attempting to trade on the brewery's good name.

First, son Matthew established Recoil brewing – see page 141 – and now, after a long legal tussle over the rights to the products, Copper Dragon is back on the up, albeit more slowly and cautiously this time around. Re-establishing their customer base has been firstly a case of

assuring them that theirs is the real deal: "We had to literally knock on the door of every public house," says Steve.

It helped that brewing legend Dave Sanders lives around the corner from their new home in Keighley and was happy to come back on board to revive the recipes which he helped create. Amber-coloured **Best Bitter** (3.8%) is a refreshing beer of genuine taste and substance with a beguiling sweet aroma and some bitter bite in the finish. Firm and malty **Scott's 1816** (4.1%) is given fruity sharpness by Slovenian and Styrian Goldings hops; pale straw coloured **Silver Myst** (4%) is to all intents and purposes a German styled cask lager without the excessive carbonation of some big name brands. Limited editions and seasonal ales extend the range; the familiar logo of a fearsome dragon guarding a copper brewing vessel makes them very easy to spot.

That continual dialogue with the landlords is now paying off, as are contracts which are putting Copper Dragon into the big supermarkets, while a move to new premises in Silsden is on the cards for later in 2019. Says Steve: "Now we just want to concentrate on doing a great job, providing good quality at a fair price."

Father and son Steve and Matthew Taylor with brewer Dave Sanders, right.

Golden Pippin (3.9%)

This remains the Copper Dragon pièce de résistance, a "go-to" beer for drinkers seeking a sessionable Yorkshire blonde. It has the clear golden colour that the name suggests, and though it has only a moderate wisp of lemon in the aroma, it bursts on the palate with a crisp, clean, tongue-cleansing burst of apple and gooseberry, before a long grapefruity aftertaste leaves you gagging for more. It is a Yorkshire legend, restored to greatness.

Crafty Little Brewery

Building 40, Humber Enterprise Park, Brough, HU15 1EQ; P: 01482 661393;
W: thecraftylittlebrewery.co.uk; E: hi@thecraftylittlebrewery.co.uk;
F: @craftylittlebrewery; T: @craftylilbrew

The last edition of this book reported on how Crystalbrew was going through something of a hiatus following a change of ownership at the plant close to the Humber estuary. At least two of the folk behind Crystalbrew have made a crafty move to this new brewery where the beers are predominantly animal themed, such as the sharply citric American pale ale **Wolf Bite** (4.8%) and the liquorice and blackberry accented **Black Ryeno** (4.5%). In a neat subversion of the genre, Crafty add oats to **Chamaleon** (4%) to bring a really full-bodied mouthfeel to a pale ale bursting with Citra and Mosaic hops.

Crooked Brewing Limited

The Garages, Leeds East Airport, Church Fenton, LS24 9SE;
P: 07890 526505; E: steve@crookedbrewing.co.uk; T: @crookedbrewltd

Have you heard the one about the Englishman, the Welshman, the Irishman and the Zimbabwean? This unlikely quartet established this microbrewery in 2017 at the former Church Fenton RAF base which has now been re-invented as Leeds East Airport. Already Crooked beers – the likes of sweetish golden **JoJu** (3.6%), woody red ale **Rufus** (4.8%) and flowery but firm **On T'Way** (5%) – are making their way into some of the better bars of Leeds and York. A new brewery tap in Acomb provides a permanent home.

Crosspool Ale Makers Society

442 Manchester Road, Sheffield, S10 5DR; P: 07828 869313;
E: crosspoolalemakers@gmail.com; F: @Crosspoolalemakers; T: @alemakers

Brewer Mark Booth founded Crosspool late in 2018 from the ashes of Hopscotch Craft Brewers, retaining some of the more popular brews that he and colleague Joe had created there, as well as bringing some new recipes to this fresh solo venture. Many reference local legends: red ale **Fifty One** (4.2%) takes its name from a bus route which has been unchanged for a century; cloudy golden orange-rich ale **Horatio Bright** (4.5%) namechecks a Victorian steel magnate, sweet and citric session ale **Sandygate** (3.6%) honours the oldest football ground in the world.

Black treacle lends depth to the smoky stout **Mount Zion** (4%), while double hopping affords extra substance to the mighty Imperial ale **Delph House** (7%). Honey and pineapple accented pale ale **Lost Tribe** (5.4%) recalls a headteacher who warned Mark and fellow recalcitrants against the dangers of becoming a member of the lost tribe. Crosspool is testament to the fact he heeded that warning.

Cuckoo Brewhouse

17 Piccadilly, York, YO1 9PB; F: @cuckoobrewhouse

Spark brings a little of New York to York itself, with an inspiring and funky space for creative businesses, social enterprises, food and drink. Owned by the Tapped group (see page 168) Cuckoo is Spark's very own brewery. It is believed to be the only container brewery in the world to use the decoction method to create its beers, removing a portion of the mash, boiling it, and returning it to the mash tun. The only beer I've caught up with so far is the pale and modestly bitter lager **Tamil** (3.6%).

Daleside Brewery

Camwal Road, Starbeck, Harrogate, HG1 4PT; P: 01423 880022;
W: dalesidebrewery.com; E: enquiries@dalesidebrewery.com;
T/F: @DalesideBrewery

Daleside Brewery has been producing cask ales and bottled beers since the mid-1980s, a time when micro-brewing was in its infancy, and many of the signs were suggesting that traditional British beer could be in terminal decline. It was under the stewardship of founder Bill Witty that renowned writer and brewer Garrett Oliver, the founder of New York's trendsetting Brooklyn Brewery, learned the basics here.

With brewing now led by Bill's son Craig, the cask range focusses on quality easy drinking beers, such as **Daleside Blonde** (3.9%), a full flavoured flaxen ale with a hoppy aroma, that remains popular across the brewery's heartland and beyond and **Daleside Bitter** (3.7%) a classic English bitter, copper coloured with a refreshing, crisp malt finish. Their strong dark bottled beers **Monkey Wrench** (5.3%) and **Morocco Ale** (5.5%) also have a keen following – and new products for 2019 include the gin-infused pale ale **G&P** (4%).

 Old Leg Over (4.1%)

There is something of the fruit and nut about this cheekily-named, bright and effervescent copper-coloured ale. The whispered sweetness of dried fruit and almonds dominate a taste which is definitely more mild than bitter and deliciously easy drinking. Its malty, peaty nature develops further in the aftertaste and rather puts one in mind of a fine Scotch and in the mood for just a little more Leg Over.

Dark Horse Brewery

Coonlands Laithe, Hetton, BD23 6LY; P: 01756 730555;
W: darkhorsebrewery.co.uk; E: richard@darkhorsebrewery.co.uk;
F: @darkhorsebrewery

Owner Richard Eyton-Jones already had some impressive breweries on his CV – Goose Eye and Old Mill in Yorkshire, St Peter's and Old Cannon in Suffolk – before he and wife Carole established Dark Horse Brewery in pretty Hetton in 2008, using their own borehole for water. And since 2016, their four beers **Hetton Pale** (4.2%), **Craven Bitter** (3.8%), **Night Jar** (4.2%) and **Blonde Beauty** (3.9%) have become permanently available. Hetton's renowned Angel Inn is perhaps the perfect place to sample these local brews, though they reach pubs across the Dales.

 Hetton Pale Ale

This clean-tasting, slightly sweet and peachy 4.2% pale ale could hardly have had a more favourable introduction; its inaugural brew won the ITV series *Yorkshire's Perfect Pint* in 2008. Available in bottle, cask and keg, it continues to deliver on the uncomplicated values which took that prize. It pours an attractive golden colour with some seductive citrus in the aroma, before the deeper substance of malt and caramel emerge in the taste of a very easy-going Yorkshire ale.

47

Darkland Brewery

Unit 4C, Ladyship Business Park, Mill Ln, Halifax, HX3 6TA;
P: 01422 320100; W: darklandbrewery.co.uk;
E: hello@darklandbrewery.co.uk; F/T: @darklandbrewery

With its onsite bar, the unit vacated by Boothtown Brewery was a perfect space for brewer Gavin Riach to indulge a passion for brewing first nurtured in a purpose-built brew cabin at home. The beer names betray a passion for Norse mythology; they include the well-balanced amber ale **Othala** (3.3%), the creamy chocolate porter **Drakkar** (4.5%) and the US-influenced IPA **Jera** (5%) whose huge hop character is derived from late-hopping in the brew. All the beers are vegan, and the first seasonal ale **Pale Green** (4.4%) was brewed from organic hops grown in Gav's garden.

Though Darkland only emerged onto the scene late in 2018, their beers are already making their presence felt in the HX and BD postcodes with regular orders from the Jacob's Well in Bradford, The Fox and Goose in Hebden Bridge and Industry Barista in Haworth. Several, including **Blackcurrant Drakkar** (4.5% ABV) and ruby **Wolfenbräu** (4%) are available in bottle. A future beer will honour local legend Percy Shaw, whose reflective cat's eyes were first manufactured close by.

Darkland's own Pallet Bar, with its six handpulls and three keg lines, seats around 50 inside and out and is open on Friday and Saturday evenings.

Dead Parrot Beer Co

*44 Garden Street,
Sheffield, S1 4BJ*

Naming your blueberry pale ale **Norwegian Blue** (4.7%) should certainly attract fans of Monty Python to this newcomer to the Sheffield scene, which opened in October 2018. Based in an old industrial

Pine in from the fjords – the impressive brewkit at Dead Parrot

unit near the city centre, brewer Mark Simmonite uses kit which had originally been purchased for Aardvark Brewery, but had never been used. His other beers include the floral and biscuity **Aurornis Xui** (4.6%) and the liquorice and caramel stout **Kato Nwar** (4.8%).

Don Valley Brewery

*Unit 3, Canalside Industrial Estate, Mexborough, S64 9HU;
P: 01709 580 254; W: donvalleybrewery.co.uk;
E: sales@donvalleybrewery.co.uk; F: @donvalleybrew*

Debbie Harry strikes a provocative pose on the pump clip for **Atomic Blonde** (4.3%), the latest addition to the core range of a brewery established in 2016, using equipment salvaged from the former Owenshaw Mill Brewery in Sowerby Bridge. Boss Richard Padmore, whose redundancy payment after years working in IT provided the opportunity to kickstart the new canalside venture, describes this one as a vibrant refreshing blonde ale with punk overtones, though its styling is in marked contrast to the three others in the range, with their deep petrol blue designs. Some interesting spice notes add interest to the simple crisp blonde ale **Hitchcock** (3.8%), there's an earthy coarseness to the deep brown malty stout **Gongoozler** (4.1%), while **Bit o'That** (4%) is a straight up, no-nonsense dark Yorkshire bitter.

49

Doncaster Brewery

7 Young Street, Doncaster, DN1 3EL;
P: 07921 970941; W: doncasterbrewery.co.uk;
E: doncasterbrewer@gmail.com;
F/T: @donnybrewery

The 2012 St Leger Festival saw the launch of a brewery built from scratch over the course of nine months by engineer turned brewer Ian Blaylock. He runs it with wife Alison; both are Donny born and bred and – apart from regular appearances at nearby festivals – their beers are sold exclusively through their excellent town centre tap, which also boasts more than 150 European bottled beers and a cracking wine list. In 2018 it was the town's CAMRA pub of the year for 2018 and Yorkshire's cider pub of the year. All the beers are named after things related to Doncaster – people, places, historic events and locomotives. They include their surprisingly carbonated caramelly **Sand House Blonde** (3.8%) and the darker, sturdier **Cheswold** (4.2%). These are available in bottle along with a range of occasional brews such as **St George's Minster Pale** (4%), **Mucky Bucket Black Pale** (5%), **Stirling Single Coffee Stout** (4.5%) and **1194 Charter Porter** (5.5%).

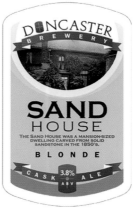

Eagles Crag Brewery

Unit 21, Robinwood Mill, Burnley Road, Todmorden, OL14 8JA;
P: 01706 810394; W: eaglescragbrewery.com;
E: sales@eaglescragbrewery.co.uk; F: @eaglescragbrewery

Brewers Dave Mortimer and Chris Milton have more than 30 years' brewing experience between them. Their eight-barrel brewery which was named after a local landmark and based in an old textiles mill, began its regular production in 2017 based around a core range of four cask and bottled beers which can now be found in pubs and bars either side of the Pennines.

Their biggest seller is well-balanced **Pale Eagle** (4%) which has already garnered a string of awards. Amber **The Eagle Has Landed** (4.6%) derives its notable piney and floral flavours from Cascade, Chinook and Simcoe hops, and is balanced with some sturdy malt, while **Eagles Feather** (3.8%) is a paler, lighter take on the same recipe.

Firm, strong **Bald Eagle** (6.9%) draws bags of pithy punch from Citra and Mosaic hops while the less potent malty best bitter **Eye of The Eagle** (4.3%) develops a lovely resiny bitter finish. Deep ruby porter **The Eagle of Darkness** (5%) has some heady chocolate and coffee character, while **Golden Eagle** (4.7%) is a generously-proportioned sharply citrus American-hopped blonde bombshell.

Many breweries now do a changing pale, based on different combinations of hops; few have so splendid a name as **Alter Eagle** (4.5%).

There's a certain symbiosis between the brewery and the local ecosystem. Spent hops are used to improve soil fertility in planters around the town, spent yeast is put to work in local compost bins, and a nearby pork farm fattens its pigs on Eagles Crag malt.

East Yorkshire Beer Co

Unit 2A, Tokenspire Business Park, Beverley, HU17 0TB; P: 07456 063670;
W: eastyorkshirebeer.co.uk; E: steve@eastyorkshirebeer.co.uk;
F: @eastyorkshirebeer

This new brewery was in the process of starting production as the first edition of this book went to press and in the past couple of years has really established itself on the local scene. It makes great play of using East Yorkshire spring water in all its brews, and an amazing ten different grains – black, chocolate, roast barley, crystal malt, pale malt, caramalt, wheat, torrified wheat, oats, and flaked barley – combine in the **Full Measure Porter** (4.3%). **Top House** (3.8%) is a sweetish, traditional mild, while **The Earl** (4.5%) hails from the softer, more nuanced end of the IPA spectrum. Each of these is named after long-lost local pubs; the onsite taproom allows visitors to graze the whole range. Brew days allow would-be brewers to get hands-on with the process while mail order brew packs provide the ingredients to recreate the experience at home.

🍺 Star of the West (4.5%)

The Star was a popular mock Tudor pub in Hull's West Street which was demolished 20 years ago to make room for a new shopping centre. Its name is revived both in a pub in nearby Trinity House Lane and in this sharp, refreshing, cold-filtered German-style pilsner, a surprisingly good, locally-brewed antidote to some of the ubiquitous big brand lagers.

Elland Brewery

Heathfield Industrial Estate, Elland, HX5 9AE; P: 01422 377677;
W: ellandbrewery.co.uk; E: info@ellandbrewery.co.uk; F/T: @ellandbrewery

Two microbreweries came together to establish Eastwood and Sanders in 2002 – and despite changes of ownership, location and personnel, it continues to do all the important things consistently well. Best known for its **1872 Porter**, CAMRA's Champion Beer of Britain in 2013, Elland's core range also includes the sharp **Beyond the Pale** (4.2%), fruity best bitter **Nettle Thrasher** (4.4%), premium pale **Gone Viral** (4.5%), restful and sessionable **Elland Blonde** (4%) and the slightly anaemic, spicy, wheat beer influenced **White Prussian** (3.9%). A roster of seasonals shakes up the choice on a regular basis.

 1872 Porter (6.5%)

1872 was the year of the *Mary Celeste*, the first FA Cup Final – and the original recipe for this rich and treacly porter. You know you are in for a treat as soon as you start to pour the beer, releasing some enticing caramel. Almost opaque jet black in the glass, it settles beneath a foaming ivory head, inviting you to dive in. Once there, your palate is bathed in a silky blanket abundant in the luxurious array of flavours symbolic of a great porter. There is dark chocolate, the bitterness of espresso, soft malt, red wine and a smokiness which lingers in the top of the mouth as a final sweetness slowly develops on the throat. It's wonderful – and if you can ever find it in a wooden cask, drink the lot.

Empire Brewing

The Old Boiler House, Unit 33, Upper Mills, Slaithwaite, HD7 5HA;
P: 01484 847343; W: empirebrewing.com; E: empirebrewing@aol.com;
T: @empirebrewinguk

The Beverley family's brewery began life more than a decade ago in a converted garage where the first brew was American-hopped pale ale **Strikes Back** (4%) which remains a part of the range to this day. They have since upped-sticks to a picturesque canalside location where they produce their thirst-quenching zesty session ale **Golden Warrior** (3.8%), dark and dry **Porter** (5%) and tropically hoppy **Smoking Pistol** (4.3%).

 Moonrakers (3.8%)

Long before Ian Fleming, the original Moonrakers were wily Somerset villagers who, when caught by the excisemen attempting to retrieve hidden brandy barrels from a pond, pretended to be clueless yokels attempting to rake in the reflection of the moon, mistaking it for a large cheese. They have lent their name to this wonderful dark mild whose extravagant cocktail of ten different malts creates a luxuriant, chocolatey delight.

Exit 33 Brewing

Unit 7, 106 Fitzwalter Road, Sheffield, S2 2SP; P: 0114 270 9991;
W: exit33.beer; E: office@exit33.beer; F: @exit33brewing

The Harlequin on the north side of Sheffield City Centre is probably the ideal place to work your way through the formidable range of a brewery named after the motorway junction which brings traffic towards the centre of Sheffield.

It starts with the sessionable **Thirst Aid** (4%) and progresses via the classic dark Yorkshire bitter **Northern Best** (4.2%) and the dazzlingly citric **Hop Monster** (4.5%). **Blonde** (4%) is an easy-drinking German lager-hopped pale ale, while the vegan-friendly unfined **Oat Stout** (5%) boasts coffee and chocolate flavours and a cushioned silky feel derived from a hefty dash of oats in the brew.

Several offer homage to the hops used in the brew, like the tropical fruit pale ale **Mosaic** (4.1%), lemon-accented **Centennial IPA** (5%) and juicy, piney, resinous **Simcoe** (5.1%).

Eyes Brewing

22 Rawson Road, Bradford, BD1 3SQ; W: eyesbrewing.com;
E: info@eyesbrewing.com; F/T: @eyesbrewing

Established in 2016, Eyes started out as a cuckoo brewery, but late in 2018 found a permanent home and brewery tap in the premises sadly vacated by Bradford Brewery. There they have continued to focus solely on wheat beers inspired by German tradition, modern innovation and long-forgotten English styles. As well as brewing classic wheat ale styles, like their 5.2% **Hefeweizen,** Eyes also have a reputation for experimentation which has given us the low alcohol white IPA **Aquarius** (2.7%), the pink grapefruit, peppercorn and rock salt Gose **Himalaya** (4.4%) and the pale **Gem State** (4.4%) which harnesses trendy new US hop Idaho 7.

Fernandes Brewery

5 Avison Yard, Kirkgate, Wakefield, WF1 1UA;
T: 01924 291709; W: www.ossett-brewery.co.uk;
E: brewery@ossett-brewery.co.uk; T: @fernandesbrewer

Established as a brewpub in 1997, the exotic-sounding Fernandes was one of the early names in the vanguard of Yorkshire's brewing revolution, bringing to this former maltstore an exciting taste of things to come.

Though still on the same premises – where a lack of mains drainage means that all the waste water has to be manhandled to the drains – Fernandes has been owned by Ossett Brewery for a decade, providing them with a much broader reach for their beers, well beyond their taproom and Wakefield heartland.

Two of their dark beers, the dry and chocolatey **Malt Shovel Mild** (3.8%) and complex, sweet smoky stout **Black Voodoo** (5.1%) have garnered a string of awards, though their other regular beers – the pale and spicy **Centaur** (4.5%), smooth and sessionable **Ale To The Tsar** (4.1%) and robust roasted malt **Double Six** (6%) are also worth a try.

Mind you, with 90 different brews produced every year, Fernandes offers the curious drinker almost endless choice.

Frisky Bear

2a Queen Street, Morley, LS27 9DG;
W: friskybear.com;
E: carl@friskybear.com

Home brewer Carl Saint established Frisky Bear in 2016, moved to Oscars Bar in Morley a year later, and now provides local pubs and bars with quality US-style craft beers. **Grizzly Bear** (4.5%) roars with a rush of juicy fruit aroma, heralding a blast of mango, blueberry and tropical fruit before a spicy, piney finish. **2pt Conversion** (6.3%) is a hazy, straw-coloured, dry-hopped New England juice bomb of an IPA.

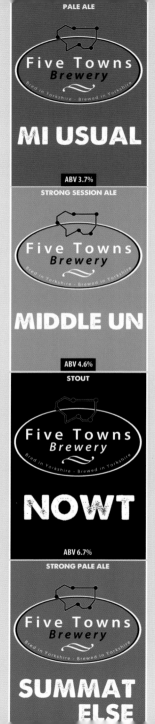

PALE ALE

MI USUAL

ABV 3.7%

STRONG SESSION ALE

MIDDLE UN

ABV 4.6%

STOUT

NOWT

ABV 6.7%

STRONG PALE ALE

SUMMAT ELSE

Five Towns Brewery

651 Leeds Road, Wakefield, WF1 2LU;
P: 07934 474180; W: fivetownsbrewery.com;
E: fivetownsbrewery@googlemail.com;
T: @fbrewery

Based in a converted garage in Outwood, Five Towns brew three times a week – producing thirty nine-gallon casks of multi-award winning ale that has gained a following far beyond the traditional five towns of Normanton, Pontefract, Featherstone, Castleford and Knottingley.

The regular beers bring local dialect to the bar: **Owt L Do** (4.6%) is a rum-fortified mild, hefty stout **Nowt** (6.7%) brims with roasted malt and coffee flavour, and prodigiously strong IPA **Summat Else** (7.2%) has a strong tropical fruit nose with gooseberry and maple syrup flavours. They don't skimp on the hops – even entry level pale **Mi Usual** (3.7%) features Nelson Sauvin, Comet and Citra while stronger session ale **Middle Un** (4.6%) dazzles with Perle Mosaic and Nelson Sauvin. A bewildering list of specials and seasonals refresh the range while a small quantity of each brew finds its way into bottle.

Straw-coloured **Sweet Thing** (5.6%) is a crisp IPA with surprising levels of carbonation – and though it does carry some of the sweet, summery fruit notes characteristic of the uber-fashionable Huell Melon hop, there is some firm, bitterness which persists into a long aftertaste.

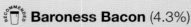 **Baroness Bacon** (4.3%)

Miner's daughter Alice Bacon, was born in Normanton, steeped from an early age in the principles of the Labour Party and delivered her first political speech at just 16. She was a Leeds MP from 1945 to 1970, a party chairman and a minister of state, before being raised to the peerage on her retirement from the Commons.

The crisp bottle-conditioned blonde ale which takes her name has a fresh lemon aroma, perhaps more body than you might expect and just a tender refreshing bitterness as it dies away. It was commissioned by the Forgotten Women of Wakefield project to keep the memory alive of a pioneer who worked for welfare, social and education reforms. How shockingly these seem to have gone out of fashion.

Fuggle Bunny Brewhouse

1, Meadowbrook Park Industrial Estate, Halfway, Sheffield, S20 3PJ;
P: 07813 763347; W: fugglebunny.co.uk; E: wendy@fugglebunny.co.uk;
F/T: @fugglebunny

Fuggle Bunny's innovative marketing strategy marries a story about an inquisitive rabbit to a catalogue of innovative quality beers, taking a quite radical new approach to getting noticed. Each of the brewery's nine beers is a chapter, the ingredients used are weaved into the story as the products of one bunny's search for excellence. The story starts with the malty, sweetish amber **New Beginnings** (4.9%) and progresses via the more markedly hoppy and citric **Cotton Tail** (4%), the moderately bitter IPA **24 Carrot** (6%), the imperial stout **Russian Rarebit** (5%). Since the first edition of this book, the American Pale Ale **La La Land** (3.9%) has been added to the story, as has the first brewery tap, Fuggle's Chapter One in Worksop.

Gene Pool Brewing

Unit 6, 23 Arthur Street, Hull, HU3 6BH; P: 07760 669157;
E: info@genepoolbrewing.com; W: genepoolbrewing.com;
F/T: @genepoolbrewing

Eye-catching pump clips help the beers from the crowd; their claim to be "genetically superior" is an interesting one, at a time when an enthusiasm for the organic has gone hand-in-hand with concerns about genetic modification. The theme continues with sturdy, maltloafy **DNAle** (4.5%), while the big peach and passion fruity **Paleo** (3.9%) and dark, dry, herbal **Primordial Ooze** (4.7%), trace back our origins further still.

GEEVES BREWERY
CLEAR CUT
4.4% ABV
AWARD-WINNING
EXTRA PALE
YORKSHIRE

GEEVES BREWERY
THE DOUGHBOY
FULL-FAT
VANILLA PORTER

GEEVES BREWERY
FULLY LADEN
6.0% ABV
WORLD IPA
YORKSHIRE

GEEVES BREWERY
THE NIGHTMARE
8.0% ABV
IMPERIAL SERIES
IMPERIAL STOUT
YORKSHIRE

GEEVES BREWERY
ROCOCO
3.6% ABV
AWARD-WINNING
CHOCOLATE MILD
YORKSHIRE

Geeves Brewery

Unit 12, Grange Lane Industrial Estate, Carrwood Rd, Barnsley, S71 5AS;
P: 07859 039259; W: geevesbrewery.co.uk; F/T: @geevesbrewery

Home brews perfected on their houseboat formed the backbone of a
commercial brewery established on an industrial estate west of Barnsley
by Harry and Peter Geeves. Eight years on, and their core list includes
the oaky, coffeeish, malty **Smokey Joe** stout (5%) and the muscular IPA
Fully Laden (6%). These are augmented by a host of interesting
specials which include sweet vanilla porter **Doughboy** (5.2%) and the
decadent imperial stout **Nightmare** (8%). Its combination of full flavour
and moderate alcohol content saw **Rococo** (3.6%) named Sheffield's
Champion Mild in 2014; attractive, eye-catching Geeves pump clips are
a welcome sight on any bar.

 ## Clear Cut (4.4%)

Bags of American hops define this clean-tasting pale ale, with its lemony
nose, grapefruity resinous eruptions on the tongue and its long and
lingering bitter-sweet finish.

Ghost Brew Co

Tong Business Centre, Otley Road, Baildon, BD17 7QD;
P: 0113 418 2002; W: ghostbrew.co.uk; E: josh@ghostbrew.co.uk;
F: @ghostbrewco; T: @ghostbrewing

Operating from premises once occupied by the much-missed Baildon Brewery, Steve Crump and James Thompson blend brewing and phantasmagoria to create beers such as session IPA **Spectre** (4.4%) and its bigger, harder cousin **Phantom** (5.3%). With its noticeable bubblegum aroma, the ghostly pale **Wraith** (3.8%) rattles biscuity malt and passion fruit along the dimly-lit corridors of the palate before slipping gently into the shadows with a haunting dry and bitter finish.

Golcar Brewery

60a Swallow Lane, Golcar, Huddersfield, HD7 4HT; P: 01484 644241;
W: golcarbrewery.co.uk; E: golcarbrewery@btconnect.com

The Rose and Crown in Golcar is the ideal place to sample beers from a brewery which has been around for the best part of two decades, but whose capacity remains at just five barrels a week – and dropped briefly to zero with the departure of assistant brewer Jonny Holmes. But long-time brewer John Broadbent awakened Golcar from its slumbers with an old favourite at the start of 2019, the pale and modestly bitter **Weavers** (4.7%).

The village west of Huddersfield is named after St Guthlac, an early Christian saint who preached here in Saxon times. His name is venerated in the full-bodied, big-tasting **Guthlacs Porter** (5%); other beers include a moderate strength trio – the neatly-balanced **Town End Bitter** (4%), roasted, sweetish **Golcar Dark Mild** (3.6%) and the floral, biscuity **Pennine Gold** (4%).

Goose Eye Brewery

Unit S Castlefields Ind. Estate, Crossflatts, BD16 2AF; P: 01274 512743;
W: goose-eye-brewery.co.uk; E: info@goose-eye-brewery.co.uk;
F/T: @gooseeyebrewery

Three generations of the Atkinson family work at this popular brewery which was one of the pioneering new-generation micros when it opened in 1991, and has recently relocated from Keighley to nearby Crossflatts. Rooted in the traditional end of the market, their real ales include the moreish American light ale **Spring Wells** (3.6%), roasted malt and chocolatey mild **Black Moor** (3.9%), premium strength English bitter **Pommie's Revenge** (5.2%) and the big-bodied fruit and liquorice **Over and Stout** (5.2%). The massively hopped and grapefruity **Chinook Blond** (4.2%) demonstrates a willingness to move with the times. It's their biggest seller.

Great Heck Brewery

Harwinn House, Main Street, Great Heck, Goole, DN14 0BQ;
P: 01977 661430; W: greatheck.siba.co.uk; E: info@greatheckbrewery.co.uk;
F: @greatheckbrewery; T: @greatheckbrew

Co-founder Denzil Vallance runs a brewery with a quirky attitude, determined independence and a decided preference for American hops. His website proclaims: "Each recipe is crafted by beer lovers, for beer lovers – accountants and marketeers don't get much of a look in." Heaps of the finest English chocolate and crystal malts go into creating the dark and silky smooth session bitter **Dave** (3.8%) while **Amish Mash** (4.7%) fuses German Weizen yeast and American IPA hops to create a cloudy wheat beer with more citrus and banana than your average greengrocers. Other beers include pale thirst-quencher **Mercy** (4%), dark IPA **Black Jesus** (6.5%) and aromatic **Citra** (4.5%) which is a showcase for this dazzling American hop. Several are available in bottle.

 Yakima IPA (7.4%)

Great Heck this is a strong beer! Named after the Washington State valley which provides the hops for this sweet, rich-textured, chestnut brown ale, Yakima is Denzil's super strength IPA. The aroma is surprisingly understated, but the beer really announces itself with a blast of toffee and blackberries on the palate, which develops into a really long dry aftertaste.

Great Newsome Brewery

Great Newsome Farm, South Frodingham, Hull, HU12 0NR;
P: 01964 612201; W: greatnewsomebrewery.co.uk;
E: enquiries@greatnewsomebrewery.co.uk;
F: @greatnewsomebrewery; T: @greatnewsome

Four generations of the Hodgson family have farmed the fertile soil of Holderness, roughly half way between the suburbs of Hull and the bracing, windswept, shifting spit of the Spurn coast. They diversified into brewing in 2007 and have since garnered an enviable reputation for beers such as the sweetish **Liquorice Lads Stout** (4.3%) and a range of seasonal cask beers such as the classic pale **Yan Tan Tethera** (3.5%), named after a traditional farmers' rhyme for counting sheep.

Honouring the local dialect name for a hedgehog, **Pricky Back Otchan** (4.2%) is a lemony, nutty, ale whose significant substance lends the impression of a beer a good deal more potent; silky, amber, biscuit-scented **Frothingham Best** (4.3%) distributes lavish warming malt and the bitterness of berries and green apples in roughly equal measure.

🍺 Sleck Dust (3.8%)

I was expecting something smoky, dirty and dark, perhaps subliminally imagining "sleck dust" to be the thick black air, pregnant with coal dust, breathed in by colliers working the seam.

It turns out that the dust referenced here is actually something thrown up on Yorkshire's sunny smiling surface, rather than its dark-hearted underground. Earlier incarnations of the label offer a clue, showing a combine harvester reaping the grain on a sun-kissed summer's day – no doubt stirring a fug of dust into the air as it goes. A recent redesign of Great Newsome's labels gives greater prominence to the name of the beer, which is joined simply by their logo of the brewery dog. No doubt this offers some consistency on the supermarket shelves, but is less pretty than its artistic predecessors.

No matter, Sleck Dust proves to be pale blonde with a thick white head, some pithy zest in the aroma and a refreshing, slightly floral taste, with some bready, yeasty notes, all zipped around by some significant carbonation.

Great Yorkshire Brewery

Main Street, Cropton, YO18 8HH; P: 01751 417330;
W: www.newinncropton.co.uk/the-brewery/; E: info@newinncropton.co.uk

Beer has been brewed in this moors village since before the Civil War and, in recent decades, Cropton Brewery became a Yorkshire legend, producing from a microbrewery behind the New Inn a host of fabulous beers – favourites like King Billy Bitter, Scoresby Stout and Monkman's Slaughter – which could be enjoyed either in the brewery tap, or further afield.

Now re-branded as Great Yorkshire, whippets, cricket bats and a pigeon have become appropriate motifs on the label, with the bottletops crossed with a black and tan check like a Yorkshire flat cap. Few beers from the previous roster have survived into the brewery's new guise. Instead, gently bitter and thirst-quenching **Pale** (3.8%) is a bright deep gold with a determined creamy head, a conciliatory, understated aroma and a nicely balanced taste that boasts just a suggestion of gooseberry. Pale and piney **Yorkshire Lager** (4.2%) delivers more firmness, bitterness and substance than some mainstream 5% continental lagers can offer. The brewery runs daily tours.

🍺 Great Yorkshire Blackout (5%)

Dark as night, Blackout glows with a faint hint of red when it's held up to the light. A lively tan head forms above the beer, some lively effervescence distributing an attractive caramel aroma. This sweetness continues to the palate where there are some suggestions of dandelion and burdock, chocolate and vanilla. Its mouthfeel is slightly thin, though this lends crisp, palate-cleansing characteristics to a beer which is pleasant and refreshing yet feels just a little insubstantial. Only in the aftertaste does any real bitterness emerge.

Half Moon Brewery

Forge House, Ellerton, York, YO42 4PB; P: 01757 288977;
W: halfmoonbrewery.co.uk; E: info@halfmoonbrewery.co.uk

Tony Rogers worked in engineering and IT for many years, while quietly honing his skills as a home brewer. Now, behind sage green garage doors in this cul-de-sac village south of York, and using tanks salvaged from a shampoo factory, his five-barrel brewery produces an interesting choice of beers which are distributed across Yorkshire in cask and bottle. Until 1969, this was the blacksmith's workshop, a fact honoured by amber, lightly spiced and lemony **Old Forge Bitter** (3.8%). American Cascade hops lend a significant blast of grapefruit to **F'Hops Sake** (3.9%), while Bramling Cross adds dark berry notes and a rounded, fruity bitterness to **Blonde** (4.2%). At Christmas watch out for multi-hopped IPA **Blitzen** (4.3%) and **Figgy Pudding** (5.2%), a luxuriant dark porter full of figs and all things nice, while the bright **Honeymoon** (4.8%), with its sweet undertones of local unpasteurised honey, plays to the lunar theme.

🍺 Dark Masquerade (3.6%)

Despite its moderate strength, this full-bodied brown ale is a robust cocktail of dark chocolate, cloves, bitter orange marmalade and liquorice. The aroma is not unlike that of a wheat beer and there's something of that clovey, banana experience on the palate, before some earthy bitterness and interesting smoky notes emerge in the finish. On a recent visit to Half Moon's tiny taproom the beer was being imaginatively served with segments of Guppy's Chocolate Orange Shards – a good match. A renowned favourite in the region it can always be found on the bar in The Beehive, Shipley and Kelham Island Tavern, Sheffield.

Halifax Steam Brewery

Southedge Works, Hipperholme, Halifax, HX3 8EF; P: 07506 022504;
W: halifax-steam.co.uk; E: info@halifax-steam.co.uk;
F: @halifaxsteam; T: @cockothenorth

Originally based in nearby Brighouse, **Halifax Steam Brewery** moved to Hipperholme, just east of Halifax in 2002, where a five-barrel plant produces a changing range of beers which are predominantly sold through their own Cock O' The North pub on the same site. **Uncle Jon** (4.3%) is a nicely rounded, malty brown ale.

Hambleton Ales

Melmerby Green Rd, Melmerby, Ripon, HG4 5NB;
P: 01765 640108; W: hambletonales.co.uk;
E: office@hambletonales.co.uk;
F: @hambletonbrewery

The famous White Horse of Kilburn is the emblem of this trailblazing brewery which was originally established by Nick Stafford at the bottom of his in-laws' garden in 1991. The equine theme continues into beers such as the malty amber **Stallion** (4.2%), their own take on a traditional Yorkshire Bitter, and the easy-drinking blonde **Stud** (4.3%).

The aptly-named porter **Nightmare** (5.0%) came about when he began a new brew one morning only to realise that he didn't have all the ingredients. Even so, the creamy, chocolatey brew he cobbled-together wasn't bad – it was the first winner of CAMRA's Winter Champion Beer of Britain award and remains one of his best-known beers.

As operations director of SIBA, Nick has helped to bring a host of other small brewers into the marketplace; the Melmerby brewery has a small-scale bottling line used by other small breweries across Yorkshire and beyond.

Harrogate Brewing Co

Unit 7, Hookstone Centre, Hookstone Chase, Harrogate, HG2 7HW;
P: 07774 891664; W: harrogatebrewery.com;
E: info@harrogatebrewery.co.uk; T: @harrogatebrewco

Who said eavesdropping never did any good? For Anton Stark, it was a chance conversation overheard in a pub, where some fellow drinkers were bemoaning the fact that Harrogate didn't have a brewery named after it, that finally persuaded him to give up his job as a commercial photographer and realise a long-held dream of becoming a brewer.

In 2013, he and wife Sarah established Harrogate Brewing Company, and now its nine core beers with their railway-inspired livery can be found on tap at a growing number of pubs in and around the spa town and across a 25-mile radius. An American-influenced IPA was their first; selling it in the town's splendid Old Bell Tavern put the new brewery in position-A for attracting immediate attention.

After a spell cuckoo brewing on others' kit, the couple established their own four-barrel brewery on the east side of the town centre, where an occasional taproom allows drinkers to try the beers on-site. They include the traditional English-hopped **Cold Bath Gold** (4.4%), multi award-winning **Plum Porter** (4.8%) and mysterious, sulphurous **Horse Head Stetson** (5.9 %). Fruity **Beeching Axe IPA** (5.5%) plays to the railway theme, while lavish winter ale **Pump Room** (5.7%) honours a local

landmark whose healing waters have drawn visitors to Harrogate for centuries.

But for me, the powerful, dark and complex barrel-aged **Kursaal Imperial Stout** (7.5%) is the outstanding performer here.

Resisting the temptation to expand, Anton and Sarah prize the independence that comes with staying small: "Expanding for us would mean a massive personal investment," says Anton. "We quite like being a self-funded small Yorkshire business. Other micros are investing millions, opening city centre bars and expanding their brew kit – and good on them, there's nothing wrong with that. But we're deliberately keeping our brewery small, independent and manageable."

And he makes a virtue out of being among the county's smallest independent microbreweries by experimenting into all manner of styles. If he thinks he can sell it, he'll make it.

Haworth Steam Brewery

98 Main St, Haworth, Keighley, BD22 8DP; P: 01535 646059;
W: haworthsteambrewery.co.uk; E: haworthsteambrew@gmail.com;
T: @haworthsteam

Though the attractive bar and bistro at the top of Haworth's historic cobbled street is the shop front for this five-barrel operation, Andy Gascoigne brews his beers 12 miles away in Cleckheaton. The newest brew is the traditional, firm and bitter pale ale **Willie Eckerslike** (4.2%), the name a dialect response to the oft-asked question of whether Andy would leave Haworth, amid a series of challenges, not least subsidence and rampant woodworm, which afflicted the premises and saw them closed for more than a year.

A family business – Kelly Gascoigne leads on sales and promotions for the brewery's growing range of gins

Now back up and running, and managed by Andy's wife Mandy, beers include sessionable IPA **Hurricane** (3.6%), the amber bitter **True Tyke** (3.8%) and the zingy glinting blonde **Rascal** (4.1%). Specials are brewed for events like the Tour de Yorkshire and Haworth's 1940s week, while separate beer brand Whitechapel includes the hoppy pale **Dr Watson** (3.7%) and easy-drinking blonde **Odds & Sods** (4%).

The Gascoignes have invested heavily in the current popularity of gin, and make no fewer than 10 different varieties, some branded as Haworth Gin and some as the Miss Mollies sweetshop range, as well as their own tonics and mixers.

Helmsley Brewing Co

18 Bridge St, Helmsley, YO62 5DX; P: 01439 771014;
W: helmsleybrewingco.co.uk; E: kyle@helmsleybrewingco.co.uk;
T: @helmsleybrewing

An on-site bar and shop attracts a steady stream of visitors to a brewery which opened in 2014 and is already a favourite in the pubs of the old North Riding. English, Australian and Slovenian hops are blended into the attractive sunny **Helmsley Honey** (4.5%), but it is the two different wild flower and heather honeys, both sourced from the North York Moors National Park which dominate both its floral aroma and its graceful, luxurious taste.

Dry flaxen bitter **Striding the Riding** (4%) is the official beer of the Cleveland Way and I came across it during a trip to the Forresters Arms in Kilburn, which is one of the early pub stops in this 110-mile scenic trek through the national park and down the Yorkshire coast. Other Helmsley beers include zesty **Howardian Gold** (4.2%) and the sparky tropical fruit pale ale **HiPA!** (5.5%).

Smoky, chocolatey **Jacky Boy** (5.5%) is cut from rather different cloth: the pour is languid and oily, the jet black beer settles beneath a creamy tan head from which some subtle coffee notes emerge. But all subtlety disperses when Jacky Boy hits the palate in a headlong rush of treacle, toffee, milky coffee and dark chocolate. The addition of oatmeal to the brew lends body and substance; a cocktail of malts drives the taste, given just a little spike of sharpness by the hop content, before dusty, smoky flavours decorate a long aftertaste.

🍺 Yorkshire Legend (3.8%)

This deep russet-coloured ale blends five local malts into a toasty, caramelly, well-balanced ale which delivers all the complexity and easy-drinking character you would expect of a traditional Yorkshire bitter. Like many of the Helmsley beers, this is available in both cask and bottle.

Hilltop Brewing

Sheffield Rd, Conisbrough, Doncaster, DN12 2AY;
P: 01709 868811

Being named the Doncaster district's pub of
the year for 2019 was just the latest
accolade for The Hilltop which established
a brewhouse in the rear yard a few years
ago. The hotel is the obvious place to try
the produce, though they have begun to
make their way further afield. They include
a serene and easy-going **Blonde** (4%), a
light and faintly agricultural **IPA** (5%) and a
smooth and interesting winter warming
Bourbon Stout (5%).

Hogs Head Brewhouse

1 Stanley Street, Sowerby Bridge, HX6 2AH; P: 01422 836585;
W: hogsheadbrewhouse.co.uk; E: hogsheadbrewpub@outloook.com;
F: @hogsheadbrewhouse

During renovations of this 18th-century former malthouse in 2015, the
new owners discovered a well, and this now supplies water for a
brewhouse which recently expanded capacity to twelve barrels. Its
handsome copper and stainless steel brewing vats are on display at the
back of the building and almost all the produce is sold on the premises.
Plans are already under way to expand capacity still further by annexing
a neighbouring building and increasing the quantity sold off-site.

   White Hog (4%) is a lightly-flavoured golden session ale with a mellow
citrus aroma and taste while **Old Maltings** (3.9%) is their lightly-hopped
take on a traditional Yorkshire bitter. The full-bodied malt loaf balance of
amber best bitter **Hoppy Valley** (4.3%) is followed by a dry fruity
aftertaste, while there's a perilously easy-drinking nature to the rich raisin
and roast malt porter **Old Schnozzler** (5.2%).

   Seasonals and occasionals broaden the range by way of the clean-
tasting **Hogs Lager** (4.7%), multi-hopped **Hog IPA** (5.5%) and a full-on
Triple Chocolate Chilli Stout (6%).

Hop Studio

3, Handley Park, Elvington, York, YO41 4AR; P: 01904 608029;
W: thehopstudio.com; E: hello@thehopstudio.com;
F/T: @thehopstudio

A permanent range of ten beers, eight seasonals – and almost countless previous recipes – marks out Hop Studio as one of the more innovative, creative, experimental breweries on the scene. From his brewery and on-site taproom close to the Yorkshire Air Museum at Elvington, brewer Dave Shaw turns out some really quality ales.

Regular brews include the punchy pithy **Pale** (4%) which draws heavily on the influence of New Zealand hops; amber **Bitter** (3.9%) which brings a red-berry influence to a traditional Yorkshire session ale and the luscious vanilla-accented **Porter** (4.3%).

A year-round bottling operation has brought to market some really confident ales; for me the very best are the dark ones such as the roasted, bourbon-aged chocolate stout **Chocolat** (6.5%) and the velvetty, oak and blackcurrant **Avenoir** (6%).

Brewer Dave Shaw shows off Treason, a porter brewed specially for sale in Parliament.

Seasonal beers allow Dave to experiment still further – **Mosaic** (4.3%) is a juicy pale given extra depth and body by oatmeal; **Solstice** (3.8%) is an IPA-lager cross; fragrant **Beerjolais** (3.8%) uses the first fresh green hops of the harvest.

Horbury Ales

Brewers Pride, Low Mill Road, Ossett, WF5 8ND; P: 07970 299292;
E: jon@horburyales.co.uk; F/T: @horburyales

Founded on a one-barrel plant in 2016, Horbury decamped to a larger plant at the Brewers Pride in Ossett, though Horbury's Cherry Tree Inn remains the brewery tap. Beers include the sunshiney **First Light** (4.1%), as uncomplicated as the brewery's minimalist pump clips, and the more noticeably citric **Sundown** (5.2%). **Galena** (4.2%) is one of a growing series of single-hopped ales.

Horsforth Brewery

Unit 1a, Park Centre, Station Road, Horsforth, Leeds, LS18 5NX;
P: 07854 078330; W: horsforthbrewery.co.uk;
E: info@horsforthbrewery.co.uk; F/T: @horsforthbrewer

Mark Costello juggles three days of his regular job with being the force majeure at Horsforth, having initially produced his beers in a domestic garage before moving into new premises late in 2018. They include the hazy, tropical fruit **Horsforth Pale** (4.5%), the sessionable pale **Horsforth Blonde** (3.8%) and a brace of dark and roasty black IPAs **Aubretia** and **Night Ryder** (both 5.5%) the latter given the extra spicy kick of rye. His bottles reveal a continental influence – with two Belgian farmhouse-style saisons, the raspberry **Rubis** and rhubarb **Soleil** (both 6.2%). Banana flavours derived from the yeast dominate hefeweizen **Weiße Rose** (5.4%), dunkelweizen **Schwarz Rose** (5%) is its darker more biddable cousin.

Hungry Bear

10-14 Stonegate Rd, Leeds, LS6 4HY; P: 0113 274 0241;
W: thehungrybear.co.uk; E: thehungrybeer@gmail.com;
F: @hungrybearbrewing

Leeds's most under-rated, under-stated brewery sits above a little bar and restaurant in Meanwood, where brewer Phil Marsh has been creating interesting small-volume brews exclusively for his own customers since 2013. His bottled beers are dispensed in simple swing-top bottles without even the luxury of a label, a tiny luggage tag typed with the name of the beer and its strength allows you to know what you're drinking, before a firm push at the metal hinge releases the ceramic stopper in satisfying fashion.

Downstairs in the bar, Phil's beers are served on draught, fresh, unfiltered and unpasteurised. They include sessionable pale ale **Golden Lark** (3.8%) and the more substantial **Meanwood Pale** (5.6%) – but with each brew being little more than 70 litres, the choice varies daily, and Phil doesn't always repeat his recipes.

Those seeking deeper substance and strength might seek out the flaxen, full-bodied, effervescent **West Coast IPA** (7.2%) which has an aroma of tart green apples, and a taste packed with sweet pineapple and bitter grapefruit. The murmuring sweetness of vanilla dominates the aroma of jet black **Vanilla Bourbon Porter** (6.3%) but this soon gives way to silky smooth, dark bitter chocolate on the palate, dying away with dusty dryness on the back of the throat.

🍺 Hearthstone Strong Ale (7.2%)

Pushing back the stopper releases some of the pent-up effervescence from this dark ale of spirited strength and full-bodied, sweetish, Christmas cake flavours, with a frothing, enthusiastic head. It's packed with malt and fruitloaf tastes, which are completely dominant over any sharper, more bitter hop characteristics. It's a beautifully-constructed, heady, oily, dark and soporific winter warmer.

Ice Cream Factory

21 Fetter Lane, York, YO1 6EH; mike@theicecreamfactory.co.uk

Sessionable American-influenced **Social Pale** (4%) is an addition to the roster at this new microbrewery established in the centre of York after a period spent brewing with Jolly Sailor in Selby. Hazy pale ales **Volume 1** (6%) and **Spacecraft** (6%) were their early interpretations of the IPA style.

Imperial Club Brewery

Cliff Street, Mexborough, S64 9HU; P: 01709 584000;
W: imperialbeerclub.com; E: impbrewery@gmail.com;
F: @imperialbeerclub; T: @imperialbeerclb

The lively Imperial Club just outside the centre of Mexborough is the tap for this microbrewery and well worth a visit. It's a simple, wide-open beer hall with a stage at one end and a bar at the other; an array of musical instruments hang from the ceiling while vintage rock posters jostle for space with pump clips above the bar. Alongside three guest ales, four of the Imperial brews were available on my visit. For me, the best was the dark, smooth and slightly treacly, traditional Yorkshire ale **Classical Bitter** (3.9%). There are some admirable warming, mellow, fruity notes to the blonde ale **Nah Then** (4.5%), while the super pale **Platinum Blonde** (4%) has more of the sharp, refreshing nature that its colour suggests. New to the core range, West Coast IPA **Golden Gate** (5.5%) blends Columbus, Cascade and Citra hops, though **Stout Wi Nowt Tekken Out** (6%) remains a high octane, dark and dangerous beast.

Ilkley Brewery

Ashlands Road, Ilkley, LS29 8JT; T: 01943 604604; W: ilkleybrewery.co.uk;
E: maryjane@ilkleybrewery.co.uk; F/T: @ilkleybrewery

March 2019 saw the tenth anniversary of Ilkley Brewery – in which time they've brewed 186 different beers, won more than 100 awards, and made enough to fill three Olympic-sized swimming pools. They're marking the occasion with a series of collaborations with brewers from around the UK.

The original Ilkley Brewery and Aerated Water Company was formed in 1873, but was swallowed up by Bass and stopped producing in 1920. It wasn't until 2009 that brewing returned to the town, since when Ilkley Brewery has produced well over 100 different brews and now features on the shelves of most of the major supermarkets. Several are American-influenced like the New World influenced **Ilkley Pale** (4.2%) and the IPAs **Alpha Beta** (4.5%) and **Lotus** (5.9%). Others include emollient oatmeal stout **Hanging Stone** (5%), mild **Ruby Jane** (4%), and new fruit IPA **Fruition** (5.5%). More traditional tastes are covered by **Ilkley Blonde** (3.9%) and cheeky Tetley tribute **Joshua Jane** (3.7%).

The brewery's long-term success has been founded on the enduring pleasures of the excellent session bitter **Mary Jane** (3.5%) which takes its name from one of the protagonists of famous folk song Ilkley Moor Baht 'at. The song recounts the tale of the fair Mary Jane who goes courting on Ilkley Moor with a chap who ill-advisedly sets out without a hat – and ends up catching his death of cold. It has some fruitiness to the aroma –

After spells at Scottish brewing legends Harviestoun, Drygate and Brewdog, Alessandra Confessore joined Ilkley as Head Brewer in 2018, with a brief to develop the talents of the existing team of brewers – and extend still further their stable of beers.

lemon, peach and floral notes – but the taste is crisp, cool, refreshing, almost lager-like, and it delivers a long bitter aftertaste.

Sightings of soccer-playing wildfowl have yet to be confirmed.

 ## Rombald (4.6%)

Legend suggests that Rombald was a local giant, though the more prosaic truth is that the name is a contraction of Robert de Romille, who was given swathes of land by a grateful King William for his role in the Conquest. He gave his name to Rombald's Moor, the moorland between Ilkley and Keighley which is more commonly known – and commemorated in song – as Ilkley Moor.

Having named beers after the song's fair Mary Jane and the moor's hanging stones it was perhaps inevitable they would soon turn to old Rombald himself, though this beer seems to be influenced more by invaders from across the Atlantic than those from Normandy.

In recent years, America's beer scene has changed beyond recognition, initially influenced by northern European styles, but now feeding off itself to create a whole host of brilliant, bitter and occasionally baffling brews. Amber ale is a style I would normally associate with France – a slightly maltier, deeper, oilier beer than the simple, refreshing cold lagers long associated with the warmer parts of western Europe; in both colour and taste it is closer to a traditional English bitter.

But Ilkley have taken America's lead by creating a rich and substantial beer whose significant bitterness is anchored to a chunky caramel backbone, with suggestions of milk chocolate hidden in there too. Its aroma is light and floral, but the aftertaste lasts and lasts, drawing in some surprising dusky, earthy bitterness right at the death.

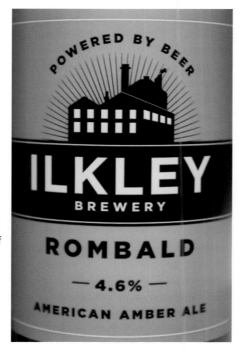

Isaac Poad Brewing

Axholme Croft, Chapel St, Cattal, York, YO26 8DY; P: 01423 358114;
W: isaacpoadbrewing.co.uk; E: beer@isaacpoad.co.uk; T: @isaacpoadbeer

Grain traders for more than a century and a half, Isaac Poad diversified into beer in 2016, building on long-established local connections to source their materials; aside from the hops, everything is grown in Yorkshire. The numbers in their beer names echo their long history – the year of their foundation and the company's previous addresses. **No 84** (4.5%) is a crisp, floral IPA whose citric attack steals stealthily across the palate; glimmering **No 86** (3.6%) manages to ally moderate strength with significant body; deep amber and nutty best bitter **1863** (3.8%) stirs warm memories of high-watermark Tetley Bitter.

Currently brewing at Hambleton Ales, they have recently added new regulars

Iron Rabbit

Leeds

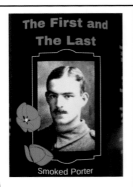

The First and The Last

Smoked Porter

Though primarily a home-brew operator, rabbit-in-chief Mike Massen took a first step towards commercial brewing in the company of Quirky Ales.

His smoky porter **The First And The Last** references the nickname of the Liverpool Pals' regiment – the first to be called up and the last to be stood down – and honours Mike's great uncle Private Arthur Seanor who died within 20 minutes of 'going over the top' on the first day of the Somme. Unlike some smoked beers, whose smokiness becomes their defining quality, here there is a subtlety, just a wisp of danger, which pervades a beer whose malty, chocolate and coffee character is equally significant. The beer was released to coincide with the centenary of the armistice, with all proceeds going to the Royal British Legion.

to the range including craft pale **No 91** (3.9%) and the chocolate and coffee porter **Piccadilly** (4.8%) – a recent winner at the Deliciously Yorkshire Awards. Each was first trialled as a special; all are now available in bottle, the first two in keg.

Recent FSQ accreditation from SIBA has seen Isaac Poad roll out into some major pubcos, and they have recently hitched themselves to the gin bandwagon too. "It's going well," brewery manager Chris Dearnley tells me. "There's no Jamaican holiday planned just yet, but if we can offer drinkers a greater range and variety it can only do us good."

🍺 **All Four** (4.2%)

Like many in the Isaac Poad range, this one has a number in the name – here it references the sizeable grain bill of barley, wheat, oats and rye used in this Irish-influenced ruby red ale. The aroma is sweet enticing caramel, and a foaming head adds an extra layer of silk to a beer of substance and warmth which develops just a little smoky bitterness at the death.

The Jolly Boys' Brewery

Redbrook Business Park, Wilthorpe Lane, Barnsley, South Yorkshire, S75 1JN;
P: 07900 403206; W: jollyboys-brewery.co.uk;
E: brewers@jollyboys-brewery.co.uk; F/T: @jollybrewery

Some of the best conversations take place in pubs. The Jolly Boys' Brewery was established in a Scarborough snug where four friends, all of them educators, realised that this was something they wanted to pursue. One of the four, Hywel Roberts, takes up the story: "The Jolly Boys have all spent their working lives contributing via their day jobs to the support of others in society. This moral drive is important to us. Couple this with a love of beer, respect for community and pride in doing a good job, we made a life-changing decision: we were going to brew beer. What more honourable and worthwhile calling

---

John Smith's Brewery

The Brewery, Tadcaster, LS24 9SA; P: 01937 832091; W: johnsmiths.co.uk;
E: customerservices@johnsmiths.co.uk

The Tadcaster Brewery was founded in 1758 and bought around a century later by John Smith, who later moved his business next door, gifting the old brewery to his nephew Samuel Smith. Now owned by Heineken, the brewery's traditional Yorkshire Squares have been replaced by conical steel fermenters producing **John Smith's Original** (3.6-3.8%) which is an uncomplicated brew of moderate malt and minimal hop character – and its rather spineless cousin **Extra Smooth** (3.6%). Between them, they outsell any other ale in the UK. With a capacity of around 3.8m hectolitres, John Smith's is one of the biggest breweries in the UK – and also produces international brands including **Kronenbourg** (5%) and **Amstel** (4.1%).

could there be? If The Jolly Boys' Brewery were a person, they'd be a listener, a carer, a mood-lifter, honest and true. They'd be non-bureaucratic and free-spirited. They'd also get a round in."

Since their first brew in 2016, the Jolly Boys have gone from strength to strength, brewing an eclectic range of ales including the robust **Jolly Collier Porter** (5%), the pale **Jolly YPA** (4.8%) and **Jolly Blonde** (4%).

Truth be told I was less impressed by the amber **Jolly Boys IPA** (5.6%), where the hops are distinctly under-played in the taste, retreating behind a taste which is simply alcoholic, without any balancing taste, neither sweet nor bitter.

Even so, their taproom, The Jolly Boys Real Ale Café, opened in 2017 and has become something of a cultural hub with live music nights, spoken word events and art exhibitions. It's the ideal place for Jolly Boys Outing.

Jolly Sailor Brewery

77 Barlby Road, Selby, YO8 5AB; P: 01757 707564; W: jollysailorbrewery.uk;
E: jollysailorbrewery@gmail.com; F: @jollysailorbrewery; T: @jollysailorbrew

Though named after the excellent Jolly Sailor pub in Cawood, the brewery itself is some five miles away in an old boxing club behind the Olympia Hotel on the outskirts of Selby. Both pubs stock the beers, several of which have been renamed and rebranded to celebrate the 950th anniversary of the foundation of the town in 2019, the stylised swan of the designs echoing the town's coat of arms.

Core products include the light and refreshing, almost lager-like **Selby Blonde** (3.8%), the amber, biscuity **Selby Bitter** (3.8%) and jet black and treacly **Selby Mild** (4%).

🍺 **Selby Pale** (3.9%)

A recent flying visit to the Olympia recently allowed me to make acquaintance with this transatlantic pale ale whose taste is shaped by the powerful influence of Nugget and Cascade hops from the US and the Maris Otter and Munich Malts from the UK. There's a slight tart tang when it first crosses the lips but the freshness of mangoes and a spicy, herby complexity nailed to that solid malty base makes this a convivial and sessionable companion.

Junction Brewpub

1 Baildon Rd, Baildon, BD17 6AB; P: 01274 582009

For drinkers who like to choose on the basis of colour, Junction's names offer an easy guide. Brewed primarily for the pub upstairs, they include significantly-hopped **Blonde** (4%), sweetish porter **Dark Thoughts** (4.6%) and fruity **Golden Splendour** (3.8%).

Keelham Farm

Gargrave Road, Skipton, North Yorkshire, BD23 1UD; P: 01756 664170;
W: keelhamfarmshop.co.uk; E: help@keelhamfarmshop.co.uk;
F: @keelhamfarmshop; T: @keelhamfarm

Evangelists for all things local, Keelham Farm stocks a vast range of Yorkshire beers, and with the help of Yorkshire Heart in Nun Monkton has dipped its toes into the water as a brewer too. Generously citric **Baaaa Humbug** (4.3%) is a pale zesty ale whose palate-cleansing lemon and grapefruit notes, anchored nicely to a muscular malty frame, were designed to cut beautifully through an onslaught of turkey, stuffing and a host of Christmas day vegetables.

Other recent specials include a **Royal Wedding Ale** (4.1%), which depicted the Royal couple as plump farmyard animals, Meghan the sheep cavorting beneath the Stars and Stripes, while the union flag flew over a pink porcine Harry. They even added a bit of ginger to the recipe, the cheeky scamps.

Kelham Island Brewery

23 Alma Street,
Sheffield, S3 8SA;
P: 0114 249 4804;
W: kelhambrewery.co.uk;
E: sales@kelhambrewery.co.uk;
F/T: @kelhambrewery

The Fat Cat in Alma Street remains the perfect place to make acquaintance with Kelham Island Brewery, which was established by academic Dave Wickett in the beer garden in 1990.

Right now, new breweries open all the time, trading on the huge popularity of beer; back then it was a more speculative venture and the city's first new independent brewery in almost a century. A pub which looks quite small from the outside has plenty of space within, with rooms either side of a tiny central bar where the Kelham Island beers have pride of place, flanked by some microbrewery rivals – and Timmy Taylor's Landlord, when I called in.

Bright yellow **Best Bitter** (3.8%) has some soft marzipan notes, there is some orange and biscuit to the amber **Riders On The Storm** (4.5%) while the sweet, big tasting and faintly popcorn-accented favourite **Pale Rider** (5.2%) has been in the roster since the early days.

Edward Wickett is carrying on the good work of his father, who died in 2012, and brewery tours pull in thirsty visitors.

Kirkstall Brewery

100 Kirkstall Road, Leeds, LS3 1HJ; P: 0113 898 0280;
W: kirkstallbrewerycompany.com; E: info@kirkstallbrewery.com;
T: @kirkstallbrew; F: @kirkstallbrewery

Few places can claim so long a history of brewing. The Cistercian monks of Kirkstall Abbey started making beer here over 800 years ago and perhaps still would be, had it not been for the disastrous intervention of a King hell-bent on a split with Rome.

Some 300 years after the dissolution, the tradition was revived in Georgian times by the first Kirkstall Brewery who unloaded their barrels directly onto barges on the Leeds-Liverpool canal which passed right behind the brewhouse and gave Kirkstall a ready means of transport to Lancashire and beyond.

For 150 years, they were a big player on the local scene, before they were closed down by giant owners Whitbread in 1983. The original stone-built tower brewery, complete with its chimney, is now home to up to 1,000 students, many of whom will no doubt have made acquaintance with beers from the new brewery which opened nearby in 2011, relocating to much larger premises in a former dairy in Kirkstall Road in 2016.

Recent massive investment in the site has seen capacity grow to 50 hectolitres, and the site is also home to the brewery's thriving beer import business. Kirkstall is also a key distribution centre for other brewers from across the UK. On my visit, in one corner of the dairy, casks and kegs from the likes of Kernel, Five Points, Hawkshead and Verdant are ready to be moved on. "We thought we would be fine on this site for the next ten years, but we've managed to fill it already," says managing director John Kelly.

Output continues to grow. Fragrant, hoppy **Kirkstall Pale** (4%) has become one of the ubiquitous beers on Leeds city centre bars; the more potent **Three Swords** (4.5%) and full-bodied **Black Band Porter** (5.5%) are others worth seeking out. The former is a clean-tasting pale ale with some suggestions of lemon and lime, the latter a smooth and big-bodied red black ale with a hearty fireside blend of milky coffee and dark fruits.

Seasonals, collaborations and single-hop IPAs are emblematic of the brewery's relentless re-invention. **Elevator** (9%) is a Belgian raspberry triple, while tequila adds a

The historic Cardigan Arms, with its famous connections to Lord Cardigan, who led the Charge of the Light Brigade, was rescued from imminent closure by Kirkstall Brewery.

dangerous edge to **Verdita** (4%) with its complex character of lime, pineapple, white wine, coriander and chilli. **Artemis** (10%) is a collaboration with Stavanger's Lervik Brewery which draws both colour and substance from its cocktail of pale and dark malts – and departs with just a spicy prickle of chilli surprise on the back of the throat.

Hedgerow (4%) is the latest in Kirkstall's sour programme and uses nettles in the brew. We made 130 kegs and sold them all in a couple of weeks. John says: "People were joking about the recipe in the brewery, and someone said, 'You might as well do a strawberry, mint and black pepper sour.' And I thought, 'Mmm, let's give it a go.'" And they have.

But the biggest seller is now the clean, generously-hopped session IPA **Virtuous** (4.5%), which is making its presence felt across the city.

Work is continuing on a long-awaited on-site pub, though recent purchases of the Sparrow pub in Bradford and Cardigan Arms in Leeds have given them a greater presence in the local off-trade. The latest development has seen them take on the elegant nine-bedroomed Black Horse in Otley, in partnership with the Brudenell, but the Kirkstall Bridge, a serial winner of Leeds CAMRA's pub of the year prize, is the perfect place to make modern-day acquaintance with a brewing history that stretches back to the dark ages.

As for the future: "It's all about more pubs," says John. That brewery founder Steve Holt is an obsessive collector of breweriana enables Kirkstall to pack their pubs with character, as well as great beers.

 Dissolution Extra IPA (6%)

Taking its name from Henry VIII's ruinous sacking of the established church, which reduced the local abbey to a stone shell, this perfect pale, modestly carbonated and deeply bitter India Pale Ale, is inspired by an IPA which was produced for export by the original Kirkstall Brewery in Victorian times. Despite its strength it remains dangerously easy-drinking; after a peachy aroma it packs in lots of hops, and a real blast of thick-cut Oxford marmalade. This is one of several Kirkstall ales now available in can or bottle.

Korruptd BrewKo

Wheatcroft Gardens, Penistone, S36 6GA; E: korruptgeoff@gmail.com;
F: @KorruptdBrewKo; T: @KBrewko

One of the newest brewers on the scene, Korruptd is also one of the smallest, with Geoff Varley producing 25-50 litre batches in his garage. The tongue-twisting range includes **Antistatik Saison**, **Hoppin Heinrich Hopfenweisse** and **Nightkrawler Imperial Stout** – though the hops, fruits and strengths are likely to differ every time. At present all the produce is bottled, but Geoff's plans for gradual organic growth include a planned move into draught production by autumn 2019.

Lady Luck Brewery

The Little Angel, 18 Flowergate, Whitby, YO21 3BA; P: 01947 602899;
F: @ladyluckbrewerywhitby

Close to the harbour and popular with the visiting Goths, this lively pub of low ceilings, stained glass and polished wood, is the perfect place to graze the Lady Luck range. They include the thin-tasting, clovey golden ale **Dream Catcher** (4.1%) and the sweetish, slightly earthy **Black Cat Porter** (4.5%).

Lazy Turtle Brewing

Meadowbeck, Barnside Lane, Hepworth, HD9 1TN; P: 01484 680598;
F: @lazyturtle22

Perhaps my radar is malfunctioning, but Lazy Turtle managed to slip under it until just a few days before this book went to press, by which time they had been brewing for almost a year. Dave Bore is a long-time home brewer and has now developed his recipes commercially, chiefly for sale in bottle. The range includes **Castaway Blonde Ale** (4.8%), **Dark Ruby Ale** (4.8%), **Riptide IPA** (5%) and **Mandarina Pale Ale** (5.5%). A Christmas saison was packaged in a 750ml corked and wired Prosecco bottle.

But the raspberry IPA **Crimson Tide** (7%) is the one I really want to try. It's a libation sensation, presumably, languid and bittersweet.

Co-owner Sam Moss and head brewer Venkatesh Iyer show off their wares.

Leeds Brewery

3 Sydenham Rd, Leeds, LS11 9RU; P: 0113 244 5866;
W: leedsbrewery.co.uk; E: info@leedsbrewery.co.uk;
F/T: @theleedsbrewery

Just as Tetley's monocled huntsman was once a fixture on the city's bars, now it seems most self-respecting real ale pubs across the city serve the crisp and refreshing **Leeds Pale** (3.8%). Full bodied dark ale **Midnight Bell** (4.8%), massively-hopped pale ale **Hellfire** (5.2%) and keg beers such as fruit-forward IPA **Monsoon** (4.1%), smoky, chocolatey stout **Gathering Storm** (4.4%) and crisp lager **Leodis** (4.6%) add further dimensions to this modern local phenomenon.

Leeds also followed Tetley's into the pub game, opening a string of highly regarded pubs including the Midnight Bell in Holbeck and Brewery Tap close to city station. Though this chain has now quietly passed into the ownership of northern giants Cameron's, Leeds Brewery beers remain a staple on the bars.

Leeds Best (4.3%)

The label describes this as a Classic Yorkshire Bitter from Leeds's largest brewer. Once the small fry in a city utterly dominated by Tetley's, Leeds Brewery has by a happy accident of timing and nomenclature, become the city's undisputed number one. As if to emphasise the point, the label features a silhouette of the city's landmarks, though wearing my University hat I would question the omission of the majestic Parkinson Tower.

This pale ale is a tad stronger than the bitter of Joshua Tetley fame, and the brewer uses that extra legroom to pack in some creamy caramel and significant maltiness, all classically balanced by the juicy bitterness of the hops. First Gold and Goldings, if you must know.

Neither side out-muscles the other, creating a beer that is both full-bodied and easy drinking. And it is in that balance that perhaps lies the brewery's success. While some others have stretched the envelope to create beers of great strength or bewildering bitterness, head brewer Venkatesh Iyer's unpretentious mainstream ales can always be relied on to deliver.

 Tetley No 3 Pale Ale (4.2%)

It would be easy to take a cynical line about the city's much-missed brewer returning after so many years to once more make beer in its traditional heartland – a story which earned me a rare front page byline in the *Yorkshire Evening Post*.

And when I first heard that Carlsberg had hooked up with Leeds Brewery to create Tetley beers in Holbeck, I did wonder whether this would be some ill-starred marketing ploy by a company too late realising the damage it caused by closing its landmark brewery.

Yet as soon as I was presented with my first pint of No 3 Pale Ale, in the grimly ironic setting of the Tetley gallery in Leeds, I could sense a genuine attempt here to create something special.

The beer recreates a recipe from 1868, using the same double strain of yeast which have lent distinctive taste and texture to Joshua Tetley's

beers since he first opened the Hunslet brewery in 1822. And as it shimmered in the glass, its white head foaming and pitting and begging to be tasted, my misgivings began to disperse. They are blown away by its crisp, dry, refreshing taste – and most of all by its fulsome full-bodied, almost chewy Tetley character.

Leeds Brewery boss Sam Moss says: "As passionate brewers, when we were approached with the opportunity of attempting to create a beer inspired by a 150-year-old recipe from the Tetley archives, it was a challenge our brew team was delighted to accept. It's been an exciting process and we're thrilled not only with the quality and flavour of the beer, but also with how faithful we've managed to remain to the original recipe."

A host of venues which Midlands-brewed Tetley Bitter will never reach are already stocking No.3 Pale Ale, hastening plans for more of Joshua's historic recipes to be reproduced, back in his own home town.

Leeds Co-Hoperative

W: leedshops.co.uk; T: @leedshops

I'm not sure if the sinister hand of climate change can be felt in this development, but hops – once the preserve of England's southern counties – are now being grown in Leeds, 200 miles from the heartlands of Kent and Sussex, Worcs and Warks. Each year, members of the Leeds Hop Growers group cultivate Cascade hop plants in their gardens and on allotments, before harvesting the chunky green flowers to create a new beer. The 2018 produce was brought together with Nomadic Brewery's expertise to create the **Gee Gee** (4.5%), the colour of a hazy sunshine, and whose name references the Green Goddess, the eye-catching brewery van. There were some prickly, zesty notes to the aroma, and a little toffee in the taste, while the Cascade hops lent some distinct bitterness to the finish.

Legitimate Industries

10 Weaver Street, Leeds, LS4 2AU; W: legitimateworldwide.com;
F: @legitimateindustries; T: @LegitimateInd

Based around the concept of a rapacious multi-national, Legitimate Industries' marketing strategy has given us beers with names like **Timeshare Scam** and **Double Agent**. Their website features a rogues' gallery of company directors – and unsavoury host of spivs, escorts and drugs suspects – and tells how the brewkit was asset-stripped from a rival. Despite their claims to having offices "from Pyongyang to Panama" even the contact details offer no clue of their real whereabouts, though the legal requirement to include an address on the cans nails them to a rather more prosaic address in downtown Burley in inner-city Leeds. The merchandise includes session IPA **Election Fraud** (4%) which has some legitimate mango and orange. The crisp, surprisingly floral **Tax Evasion** (4.4%) is probably as good a pilsner as Leeds has ever produced.

Identity Theft (5.3%)

For Legitimate Industries' faux-criminal hype to work, it has to be built around quality. Hazy yellow Identity Theft certainly delivers bags of substance – a significant dry pale ale which is packed with kiwi and grapefruit and a long aftertaste which slowly builds the warmth you might expect of a beer of this premium strength. Get it while it's legal.

Linfit Brewery

Sair Inn, 139 Lane Top, Linthwaite, Huddersfield, HD7 5SG; P: 01484 842370

Brewer Ron Crabtree was a legend in his own lifetime, which sadly ended in October 2016, when he died of throat cancer aged 79. For more than 30 years, his two-and-a-half-barrel plant had produced a number of quality cask ales before brewer Ian Bagshaw stepped into the breach, reviving many of Ron's old recipes. The Sair – pronounced "sow" – is set among steep and twisting Pennine roads west of Huddersfield; stepping inside is to enter a beautiful old time-piece, intimate, low-ceilinged, with the kind of welcome and atmosphere you'd find in one of the lovely bars on Ireland's western coast. A line of ten handpulls dispense a host of beers all produced in-house, such as the wittily-named **Janet St Porter** (4.2%) and the pale and distinctly lemony **Neck Hoyle** (3.7%), the name doubtless an homage to craft greats Beavertown.

 Old Eli (5.3%)

Of the beers I tried on a recent visit to the Sair, this well-balanced bright copper ale made the greatest impression. There's a whiff of caramel in the

aroma, and a taste packed with toffee sweetness and the indulgence of damsons, between them creating the intensity of a premium Yorkshire bitter. A regular suggested I try its darker and more powerful cousin **Leadboiler** (6.6%) – but time and the drink-drive laws prevented me enjoying this undoubted pleasure.

Little Black Dog Beer Co

Carlton Towers, nr Snaith, DN14 9LZ; P: 07495 026173;
W: littleblackdogbeer.com; E: contact@littleblackdogbeer.com;
F/T: @blackdogbeerco

Few microbreweries have such an impressive neighbour. Little Black Dog is kennelled in the former coach house of Carlton Towers, the Gothic stately home which was for generations the Yorkshire seat of the Dukes of Norfolk.

Brewing started in 2015, and now virtually all production is focussed on filling the cellars of the Doghouse, their own cafe-bar close to the south face of Selby Abbey. Bar and brewery are symbiotic, a perfect family eco-system. Nigel Kot and son Jordan brew the beers, wife Christine and daughter Emily run the bar: "We're producing just enough to keep up," says Christine.

The brewery makes great play of the fact that their cask ales are unpasteurised, unfiltered and unfined, so it would be reasonable to expect a little haze. All the same, the **Yorkshire Bitter** (3.8%) which I tried was a bright clear bronze, with the gently hoppy, refreshing nature you'd expect of this genre, with a little woodiness thrown in for good measure. Others include the smooth, coffee-and-chocolate **Oatmeal Stout** (4.5%) and newcomers **Big Red** (4.4%) and **Tidal Pale** (3.8%).

Little Critters Brewery

Unit 5, Neepsend Industrial Estate,
80 Parkwood Rd, Sheffield, S3 8AG;
P: 0114 276 3171;
W: littlecrittersbrewery.com;
E: info@littlecrittersbrewery.com;
F: @smallbatchbeers;
T: @littlecritsbrew

Barely fledglings when the first edition of this book was published, Little Critters have since added several new species of beer to their menagerie. Their growing flock now includes the crisp, refreshing, pine-accented American pale **White Wolf** (5%), the imaginatively-titled English pale ale **Malty Python** (4.8%) soporific oatmeal stout **Sleepy Badger** (4.5%) and the **Chameleon** series of single-hopped ales (5.5%).

The smooth and powerful espresso stout **King Crow** (7.2%), which delicately blends silky chocolate with the dark bitterness of roasted coffee beans, is a perfect advertisement for the qualities and abilities of this excellent new brewery. The Doctor's Orders, close to Sheffield University campus, is Little Critters' brewery tap.

Little Valley Brewery

Turkey Lodge, New Road, Hebden Bridge, HX7 5TT; P: 01422 883888;
W: littlevalleybrewery.co.uk; E: info@littlevalleybrewery.co.uk;
F: @littlevalleybrewery; T: @littlevalleyale

Beer-loving Dutchman Wim van der Spek met partner Sue Cooper while they were both cycling in Nepal – he was pedalling one way and she was going the other. After synchronising directions, the couple moved to

Yorkshire in 2005 and began peddling beers from Little Valley Brewery high above Hebden Bridge. Here their devotion to great ale and concern for the planet go hand-in-hand with producing some of the county's most interesting beers, which between them have garnered an impressive collection of awards.

Several honour Pennine placenames. There's moderately flowery and marmaladey **Cragg Vale Bitter** (4.2%), spicy, pithy, hazy **Hebden's Wheat** (4.5%) – twice a silver medal winner at the Great British Beer Festival – and the straw-coloured and floral flagship ale **Withens Pale** (3.9%) which takes its name from the windswept fell which reputedly inspired Emily Bronte, though its agreeable nature is perhaps more Cathy than Heathcliff.

There's a suggestion of white wine to the understated aroma of the anaemically-pale **Stage Winner** (3.5%) which has so exuberant a white head it might easily be mistaken for a specialist Belgian lager. It celebrates the life of Yorkshire cyclist Brian Robinson – the first Brit ever to win a Tour de France stage. The old-school, well hopped and slightly grassy IPA **Python** (6%) was drunk by Palin, Cleese et al, during their reunion gigs in 2014.

Bright ginger beer **Radical Roots** (4%) pours a bright gold with an extravagant foaming white head from which some gingery notes emerge, and some of that rootsy character continues into the taste where its backed by bags of firm bitterness, and a lovely dry aftertaste.

Stylishly packaged in a black presentation box and with a label tooled in expensive shiny gold script, **LVBX** (10%) makes great play of this as a bottle conditioned, handcrafted organic barley wine, packed with "eight superior hops and malts". Prising off the cap releases peaty and malty aromas; pouring it reveals its deep red-brown colour. If you hadn't read the label you might easily imagine this a sessionable brown ale or a mid-strength ruby porter. But those illusions are blown away when LVBX hits the palate and its whisky-like characteristics persist in a complex blend of woodsmoke and the sweetness of damsons. There

are toasty caramel notes in there, but the iron-like firmness and sheer strength of this beer ensures that it quickly begins to work a soporific alchemy on the senses, its powerful influence remaining into a long liqueur coffee aftertaste.

Many of the Little Valley ales are available in bottle, others are sold through organic and vegan wholesaler Suma – and their first keg beers are coming soon.

Stoodley Stout (4.8%)

The original monument on Stoodley Pike, above the Pennine towns of Todmorden and Hebden Bridge, commemorated the defeat of Napoleon at Waterloo – but collapsed in 1854. Its replacement was erected a few years afterwards when Crimea was added to the conflicts it recalled. Though struck by lightning many times it remains visible for miles around.

If LVBX remains Little Valley's pièce de résistance, Stoodley Stout stretches the envelope in terms of what fulness of flavour might be wrought from a dark beer of less than half that strength. Its languid, oily pour offers clues to its richness, and it forms an exuberant foaming head, from which enticing dark chocolate aromas emerge. These wash across the palate, where they're joined by plums, chocolate, a whiff of woodsmoke and the dangerous bitter nature of an espresso distilled to rocket-fuel caffeine strength. There's more bitterness in the aftertaste of a truly monumental Yorkshire stout.

Littondale Brewery

Queens Arms, Litton, Skipton, BD23 5QJ; P: 01756 770208;
E: info@queensarmslitton.co.uk; F: @queensarmslitton

The Queens Arms in Litton, north of Skipton, is home to this brewery which was first established in the early 2000s, and closed a decade later amid various changes of management at the pub, before being revived in 2017. Session ale **Littondale Pale** (3.9%) is a companionable blend of citrus and caramel, a perfect tonic after a day's walking in the Dales.

Lords Brewing

Unit 15, Heath House Mill, Golcar, Huddersfield, HD7 4JW;
P: 01484 651230; W: lordsbrewing.com; F: @lordsbrewingco

Golcar Brewery owner John Broadbent inspired three brothers to establish Lords to set up in 2015, initially using his own spare capacity but now using kit of their own. The recent purchase of new tanks and fermenters have tripled capacity, while new lab equipment and an extra delivery van each hint of big developments to come.

Beers include traditional Yorkshire bitter **Tithe House** (3.9%) with its characteristic balance of hearty malt and amiably bitter English hops. By contrast, it is the strident citric, piney influence of American hops which dominate West Coast pale ale **Mount Helix** (5%), while there are some interesting spicy notes to **Havelock IPA** (5.9%). **Odette** (6%) is an unfined, deep golden saison with a fruity and spicy flavour, brewed using Saaz hops, while amber **Chosen Man** (4.4%) leans heavily on the influence of its New Zealand hops. A taproom opens up the range to drinkers, most weekends.

🍺 **Amaro Joe Coffee Beer** (5.7%)

Lactose sugar lends an extra creaminess to this white coffee beer, which uses cold-brewed organic Amaro Gayo coffee, exported by Asnakech Thomas, Ethiopia's only female miller and exporter. Unlike most coffee beers which aim for the espresso end of the barista's range, this pale ale has the taste and finish closer to a cappuccino, given an extra chocolate twist by cacao nibs.

Lost Industry Brewing

14a Nutwood Trading Estate, Limestone Cottage Lane, Sheffield, S6 1NJ;
P: 0114 231 6393; W: lostindustrybrewing.com;
E: beer@lostindustrybrewing.com; F: @lostindustrybrewing; T: @lost_industry

Though only four years old, this family-run brewery's industrious attitude has already forged a reputation for their interesting and progressive expressions of both traditional and contemporary beers. Not having a regular brew has freed them to venture into wheat beers, sours, saisons, Belgian pales and dark ales – as well as the more familiar South Yorkshire territories of bitters, stouts, porters and pales. As we go to press, the first of Lost Industry's sour and bretted beers to be aged for a year in Bordeaux wine barrels, were being released. Boss Lesley Seaton tells me: "We're all beer geeks and we enjoy pushing the boundaries."

Loxley Brewery

Wisewood Inn, 539 Loxley Road, Sheffield, S6 6RR; P: 0114 233 4310;
W: loxleybrewery.co.uk; E: info@loxleybrewery.com; F/T: @loxleybrewery

Newcomers Loxley were established in disused storage rooms at the Wisewood Inn, north-west of Sheffield in 2018, a pub which went through the hands of all manner of pubcos, before being established as their brewery tap. Fresh water from the Loxley spring 70 metres beneath the pub forms the backbone to each of their sessionable-strength brews, whose names display a perverse lack of imagination. **Wisewood 1** (4%) is an American-style blonde featuring an alliterative range of Cascade, Centennial and Chinook hops, while New Zealand's Motueka lends its influence on the golden **Wisewood 2** (4.3%). The range meanders upward to the five-hop pale ale **Wisewood 7** (4.4%). Brewers Dave Woodhead and Michael Hampshire are planning to spread their wings with a variety of brewing styles; their twelve-barrel kit is pure Sheffield steel.

Luddite Brewery

Calder Vale Hotel, Millfield Road, Wakefield, WF4 5EB; P: 01924 275351

Given that the Luddites were hell-bent on the destruction of all things industrial, it should be barely surprising that this brewery threw production of this book into chaos by opening the day before its final copy deadline. Nearly two years had passed since planning permission was granted for part of the popular Calder Vale Hotel to be re-purposed for brewing. **Smashing Saaz** had some favourable reviews on social media – there's perhaps a technological irony there somewhere – and had I been invited to the opening, I might have been able to say more.

Magic Rock

Willow Park Business Centre, Willow Lane, Huddersfield, HD1 5EB;
P: 01484 649823; W: magicrockbrewing.com;
E: sales@magicrockbrewing.com;
F: @magicrockbrewing; T: @magicrockbrewco

Magic Rock is among a special brand of brewers who have transcended humble, locally-based beginnings to become a worldwide craft sensation – in their case sufficiently eye-catching to attract a massive buyout by Australian giants Lion early in 2019.

Though founded just eight years earlier, production grew steadily to reach around three million pints a year – plenty of which are downed in their impressive on-site taproom a short walk from the centre of Huddersfield.

Magic Rock fuses the enthusiasm of founder Richard Burhouse to the extraordinary brewing skills of Kelham Island alumnus Stuart Ross. The name references the Burhouse family gemstone business, and lends itself to an assortment of beers with a big top, freak show theme, like the pale floral **Ringmaster** (3.9%) whose moderate strength belies a beer of substance and significant fruit flavour – lemon, mango and lime. **Dark Arts** (6%) is an assertive gloopy, chocolatey, smoky stout with just a suggestion of dandelion and burdock, and there is a host of brews bearing the **High Wire** name.

Reddish-brown **Rapture** (4.6%) is among their flagship products. Characteristically for this brewery, its use of prodigious quantities of six varieties of hops generates sharp and slightly angular fruit notes to the aroma and plenty of significant juicy fruit flavour.

Though stronger than many, **Cannonball** (7.4%) is absolutely exemplary of the wonderful resurgence of India Pale Ale; its blend of resinous hops delivers a firm and complex taste, with apricot, grapefruit, peach, passion fruit and pine. Gluten-free **Fantasma** (6.5%) delivers bags of hop-heavy bitterness, cloudy **Saucery** (3.9%) explodes on the palate with such a blast of passion fruit, mango and pine it might easily be a good deal stronger.

Seasonals, specials and occasionals deliver yet more of the magic; distinctive pump clips, cans and labels make them instantly recognisable on any bar. One hopes that the new owners will allow the Magic to continue.

🍺 **Salty Kiss** (5%)

It is an unintended consequence of the phenomenal mission of the Campaign for Real Ale that brewers have been given the confidence to experiment in a variety of styles, stretching beyond established boundaries the range of beers now brewed in Britain. Which is how we get a sour German-style Gose, flavoured with gooseberry, sea buckthorn, rosehips and sea salt, created in Huddersfield in collaboration with the Danish brewer Kissmeyer.

Originally from Goslar in Lower Saxony, Gose is a regional speciality first brewed over 1,000 years ago. Made with at least 50% wheat malt, it is similar in style to other wheat beers, Belgian Witbiers and German Weisses, with the obvious difference that it uses salt water in the brew. Light-bodied and slightly carbonated, Salty Kiss pours a light and slightly hazy gold, and though a little saltiness can be discerned in the aroma, its true nature only emerges in the taste. Here your palate is treated to a sour fruity saltiness, with a dazzling array of fruit salad tastes – apple, apricot and banana, and just a suggestion of coriander.

Mallinsons Brewing Co

Unit 1 Waterhouse Mill, 65-71 Lockwood Road, Huddersfield, HD1 3QU;
P: 01484 654301; W: drinkmallinsons.co.uk; E: info@drinkmallinsons.co.uk;
F: @thecornerhudds; T: @Mallinsons

Huddersfield favourites Mallinsons have been going almost a decade now, but stepped up production with a move to a new 15-barrel plant in 2012. Rather than having permanent beers, Mallinsons produces a rolling core range which usually includes a couple of session-strength cask ales devoted to a particular hop variety and a number of key kegs.

The brewery took Beer of the Festival five times in a row at Huddersfield's Oktoberfest and can usually be found in the best local beer houses – including the brewery's own town centre taphouse the Corner – but they're widely distributed across the north.

It's worth seeking out the hazy **Motueka** (4%), whose name honours the hop variety which lends citric aroma to a significant beer of only moderate strength. Other favourites include the sharply bitter **Mosaic** (4%) and orange-accented **Amarillo** (4.2%).

🍺 Columbus (3.9%)

It's a good 500 years since Christopher Columbus discovered the Americas, but it's only in the last few decades that the drinkers of that country have fully embraced the diverse beer culture of Europe – and expanded it to be their own.

In doing so they have pushed back the boundaries of what we believed possible, creating beers of intense, diverse fruit, spice and bitter character. An industry which grew, notably in the Pacific North West, to provide American brewers with the hops capable of generating these amazing flavours, now supplies the world. In many British brewhouses, they have supplanted the trusty hop varieties grown in Kent and in England's south west.

Columbus is one of those new-breed American varieties, and it lends to this beer of dull shimmering gold and moderate strength a vibrant strident bitter character many far stronger ales fail to achieve.

Malton Brewery

5 Navigation Wharf, Malton, North Yorkshire, YO17 7AA; P: 07946 776613;
W: maltonbrewery.com; E: horsetownbeers@gmail.com; T: @maltonbrewery

Brewing started on the banks of the Derwent in Malton in 1767; this new brewery, based in a grade II listed building, maintains this long tradition and was named best new business at the Ryedale Business Awards in 2017. Suddaby's Crown Hotel is probably the best place to graze the brewery range which is based around three sessionable favourites – **Heritage Bitter** (4%), **Whitewall Golden** (4.2%) and **Middleham Heritage Pale Ale** (4.2%), along with a host of canned and bottled beers, many to a horsey theme. The misplaced apostrophe on the labels has a peculiar charm all of its own.

Meanwood Brewery

8a Stonegate Road, Meanwood, Leeds, LS6 4HY;
P: 0113 318 5821; W: themeanwoodbrewery.com;
E: baz@themeanwoodbrewery.com;
F/T: @meanwoodbrewery

Brothers Baz and Graeme Phillips started brewing in their garage before decanting the operation into the splendid two-floor Terminus bar and brewhouse in the heart of Meanwood, a suburb where a host of new premises have created a fabulous little bar crawl to rival anything the city can offer. Regular brews include malt-forward session beer **Herald** (3.9%), the amber **Shapeshifter** (5.1%) based on the hybrid ale-lager California Common style, and the big juicy New England IPA **Pilgrim** (6.6%). Determined to explore all of beer's many taste experiences, the brothers expand the range almost weekly and recent creations include the rule-defying, dry and fizzy saison **Trickster** (7.3%), the seductive oak-aged porter **Black Goddess** (4.9%), and **Exile** (3.4%), which twists the Berliner weisse genre with blackberries and oats.

Mill Hey Brewhouse

2 Mill Hey, Haworth, BD22 8NQ;
P: 01535 646823;
W: millheybrewhouse.co.uk;
E: millheybrewhouse@outlook.com;
F: @millheybrewhouse

Though the name would suggest it's brewed on the premises – and I have seen some evidence of a **Mill Hey Best Bitter** (3.7%) – it has been difficult to ascertain where this rather lovely beer and cocktail bar actually makes its beer.

Mill Valley Brewery

Unit 5, Woodroyd Mills, South Parade,
Cleckheaton, BD19 3AF; P: 07565
229560; E: info@millvalleybrewery.co.uk;
W: millvalleybrewery.co.uk;
T: @millvalley2015;
F: @millvalleybrewerytap

An on-site bar draws drinkers to Mill Valley, where production is concentrated on six moderate-strength ales including the benign and gently amber ale hoppy **Luddite** (3.8%) and the light, spicy **Mill Blonde** (4.2%). Their flagship beer is the tropical fruit session ale **Panther** (4%), while chocolate malt and roast barley lend colour and character to its darker, stronger cousin **Black Panther** (4.6%).

Milltown Brewing Co

The Old Railway Goods Yard, Scar Lane, Milnsbridge, Huddersfield, HD3 4PE;
P: 01422 610579; W: milltownbrewing.co.uk;
E: contact@milltownbrewing.co.uk; F/T: @milltownbrewing

Before this was a brewery, even before it was a railway goods yard, these premises were stables for delivery horses. The four-barrel plant was established here in 2011 and the beers regularly feature in Huddersfield pubs and those inside a 15-mile radius. **Black Jack** (4.5%) is a porter with some nice chocolatey notes, while there's a touch of spice to the refreshing and sessionable **Platinum Blonde** (4%).

Pale yellow **Bavaria** (3.9%), which draws passion fruit and lemongrass flavours from its German Hallertau Blanc hops, is a newcomer to the range, but my favourite is the dark ruby ale **Maltissimo** (5.3%) whose firm malty and vanilla character is beautifully balanced by its dry bitter finish.

A half mile north, the Dusty Miller at Longwood, with its stunning Colne Valley views, is the brewery tap; a few miles south is the brewery's second pub, the Traveller's Rest at Meltham.

Mitchells Hop House

352-354 Meadowhead, Sheffield, S8 7UJ; P: 0114 274 5587;
W: mitchellswine.co.uk; E: info@mitchellswine.co.uk;
F: @mitchellswine; T: @mitchellswines

When the neighbouring Italian restaurant closed in 2016, long-established wine, beer and cigar store Mitchells decided to expand both premises and portfolio – pressing two old yoghurt churners into a new life as fermenters at the Mitchells Hop House Brewery. Beers include earthy 'beer and beef' bitter **Butchers** (4%) and **Madness IPA** (5%) – "We must have been mad to open a brewery." says boss Frankie Mitchell.

   Independent Blonde (4%) recognises their status as a long-standing wine and spirit merchant and the exuberant, zesty and refreshing **Marilyn** (4.3%) is named after the rather kitsch statue of Marilyn Monroe which stands outside. Mitchells recently moved all their hand-bottled beers to contract bottling, giving them a new look for 2019. Well-established pub and restaurant contacts offer a straightforward route to the on-trade while their own-brew competes for attention against 400 other bottled beers on Mitchells shelves.

 **Dennis** (4.5%)

Named after the company's founder, this floral and spicy ale is anaemically pale, and has a significant effervescence as its glistens and sparkles in the glass. The head soon dissipates, though its bright lemon aroma remains, before the palate is cleansed by the crisp and refreshing assault of a beer so dangerously easy drinking it ought to carry a health warning.

Mithril Ales

Aldbrough St John, Richmond, DL11 7TL; P: 01325 374817;
W: mithrilales.blogspot.co.uk/; E: mithril58@btinternet.com

Rather than stick to a core range, brewer Pete Fenwick seems to have a restless spirit for experimentation, his regular blog posts announcing his newest creations and where to find them. Pubs in the very north of the county, and others over the border in County Durham and Northumberland, are the best places to seek out his handiwork. I found rugby-themed **Between The Posts** (3.8%) at the High Force Hotel, after a walk down to the waterfall. Though of only moderate strength, this combined the substantial and long-lasting bitterness of grapefruit with some of the sourness you might expect of a naturally-fermented Belgian beer.

Morton Collins Brewing

The Star Inn, 42 Standbridge Lane, Wakefield, WF2 7DY; P: 01924 253659;
E: gedmorton@aol.com

After being limited to appearances at local beer festivals, taking over the tenancy at The Star Inn in Sandal gave Sam Morton and Ged Collins a permanent outlet for their microbrewery which began production in 2016. Beers include the amiable, berry-ish **Wintersett Gold** (4.1%), full-flavoured stout **Stanley's Delight** (4.8%) and the malty, earthy, biscuity **Strong Brown Ale** (4.7%).

My Generation Beer Co

Wellgarth, Crosshills, Masham, HG4 4EN; P: 01765 689227;
W: mygenerationbeer.co.uk; E: hello@mygenerationbeer.co.uk;
F: @mygenerationbeer; T: @mygenbeer

Beer marketing consultant Jonny Kirkham joined forces with Black Sheep brothers Rob and Jo Theakston to create this independent venture based around a holy trinity of beer, music and pubs. The signature beer is an easy-going straw-coloured session **Pale Ale** (4.2-4.7%), and the website recommends some musical accompaniment – everything from Bill Ryder-Jones to the Kinks, last time I looked. Though recorded in 1968, the words, "We are the draught beer preservation society..." remain eerily apt.

Maharajah (5.1%)

The appropriate name of this India Pale Ale was sufficient to grab my attention, yet the story behind it is truly remarkable. In 1872, Manchester's Belle Vue Zoo bought an elephant called Maharajah from an Edinburgh menagerie which was closing, but he proved a reluctant traveller – initially destroying a railway carriage of the 10.05 Waverley-to-Manchester express. Eventually, it was decided he would have to walk, and so he did, accompanied by the great-great-grandfather of brewer Ged Morton's wife. Unveiled to mark the second anniversary of their take-over at the Star, Ged created this fresh, crisp, floral and bitter IPA, lavishly hopped with Simcoe, Citra and Cascade.

Nailmaker Brewery

Unit 9, Darton Business Park, Darton,
S75 5NH; P: 01226 380893;
W: www.nailmakerbrewing.co;
E: beer@nailmakerbrewing.co;
T: @nailmakerbrew

Paleton (4%), an elegantly-named tribute to the Tour de Yorkshire, was the first to be produced by Nailmaker, which took over where the mothballed Two Roses had left off. Its eight-barrel plant, under the same ownership as nearby pubs the Talbot and the Wentworth, has taken on some of the old recipes, while creating some new ones of its own. Pale ales **Chinook** (4.2%), **Cascade** (4%) and **Mosaic** (4%) each showcase a single hop, while New Zealand's Nelson Sauvin lends grape and gooseberry to the lovely pale ale **Auckland** (4%). **Anvil Porter** (4%) revives Two Roses' generously chocolatey Heron Porter.

Naylor's Brewery

Midland Mills, Cross Hills, BD20 7DT; P: 01535 637451;
W: naylorsbrewery.co.uk; E: info@naylorsbrewery.co.uk;
T: @naylorsbrewery

Beer has seemingly endless capacity to surprise. With Naylor's forbidding, jet-black **Pickwick Porter** (4.5%), the moment of revelation comes in the aroma, where there are some interesting sweet-peach notes – a characteristic more akin to a light fruity summer ale than one drawn from this dark, malty, smoky genre. Some of this supple juicy nature persists into the taste, but there it is soon overwhelmed by waves of black coffee, treacle and just a whiff of woodsmoke. The bitterness of dark chocolate dominates the long aftertaste of a 4.5% ABV beer which both warms and refreshes.

Stephen and Robert Naylor style themselves "The Brews Brothers". They began brewing at the Old White Bear, the pub they owned at Cross Hills in 2001, and within a few years decided to concentrate on brewing pure and simple, moving to their new home nearby.

Distributed predominantly in the west of Yorkshire and in the Dales, Naylor's have established a reputation for traditional Yorkshire ales. And the Houses of Parliament too, where their **Cratchit's Cracker** (4.2%) was the Christmas beer of choice in 2016.

Core beers include the zesty, zingy **Blonde** (4.3%), which has a touch of wheat to the recipe and the dark amber, fruity **Old Ale** (5.9%) which gains its smoothness during a long period of maturation. **Yorkshire Ale** (3.8%) is a softly-spoken, refreshing copper-coloured traditional bitter, while the deep brown **Black and Tan** (4.4%) blends their bitter and porter recipes into a mellow ale of remarkable smoothness. All of these are available in bottle.

Naylor's also produce a changing list of seasonals and specials – current offerings include a **Toffee Mild** (4.2%), given colour and sweetness by black treacle; creamy stout-ish **Obsidian** (4.2%) and the single-hopped **Chinook** (4%), which shows off that much-loved variety's piney, spicy character.

On a recent visit to the Dales I picked up a bottle of **Black Cherry**

(5.6%) in a specialist off licence with a phenomenal range of ales from the UK and further afield. Unlike some fruit beers, particularly those from the continent, where the fruit taste completely dominates, here this decadent dark ale just bears the hint of cherries as an influence. It pours like a viscous oil, topped by a big frothy tan head, and has a leathery texture with some burnt toffee tastes and just a suggestion of dandelion and burdock. It's interesting, quite challenging, but the bitterness here is that of a Haribo cherry sweet, rather than the full-on cheek-sucking sourness of a Belgian Lambic.

 ## Archie's Ginger Nectar (4%)

I had an encounter with a fairly unpalatable ginger beer from a Manchester brewery a while back. The ginger was too strident, the taste too sweet, the effect too overpowering. It was the sort of ale you suffer a half of before moving onto a traditional beer instead.

Archie's Ginger Nectar is a far better example of the genre, the effect much more subtle, the ginger adding just a spicy note of interest. By every other measure it's a crafted English ale pure and simple, refreshingly sharp, with fruit and hops dominating a taste that gathers momentum into a soothing, long-lasting aftertaste.

If you're expecting a big ginger burst in the aroma, then you'll be disappointed; here the nose is light, slight and heathery, summery, flowery. The ginger in the taste is supported by some significant hoppy bitterness, though there are some nice citric fruity tastes in there as well, before its long, rich, dry aftertaste kicks in on the back of the throat. Its ginger is less pronounced than the Lancashire version, and certainly less than its alcohol-free counterparts.

I know one reformed drinker who only sups ginger pop these days. His local landlord stocks his favourite brand specially, so he can still be a regular in his favourite boozer without ever falling off the wagon. Mind you, Archie's Ginger Nectar is good enough to send any anonymous addict back on the binge.

Neepsend Brew Co

Unit 1-3 Lion Works, Mowbray Street,
Sheffield, S3 8EN;
P: 0114 276 3406;
W: neepsendbrewco.com
E: gavin@neepsendbrewco.com;
F/T: @neepsendbrewco

Though only established in 2015, Neepsend fought off a wealth of competition to be named Champion Beer of Sheffield in 2016, with their chocolatey, coffee-ish stout **Rollabout** (4.5%), which was brewed with the Sheffield Steel Rollergirls team.

"We like to be experimental rather than constrained to a core range," head brewer Gavin Martin explains. "I've lost track but we've reached well over a hundred different beers brewed. It's probably closer to 150." Though facing some upheaval – their premises are set to be converted into flats – Gavin is confident about the future of Neepsend and the city's vibrant scene: "I think there's room for all of us," he tells me over a pint in the newly-opened St Mars of the Desert taproom. "Everyone's doing something a bit different, and there's a real appetite out there."

Blonde (4%)

This mellow and sessionable pale ale is the flagship Neepsend beer, and their only permanent brew. Hopped with Brewer's Gold, Chinook and Cascade, this delicate blonde is mellow and easy-drinking, low in bitterness and with a crisp dry finish. All the Neepsend pump clips feature Ball Street Bridge, a local landmark which is in sight of the brewery. It's actually the second – the original 1856 bridge was washed away in the disastrous Sheffield flood of 1864, before being rebuilt.

Nightjar

2 Richmond House,
Caldene Business Park,
Mytholmroyd, HX7 5QL;
P: 07412 008221;
W: nightjarbrew.co.uk;
E: jonny@nightjarbrew.co.uk;
T: @nightjarbrewco

Last time I was here, this was Slightly Foxed Brewery, but a change of name, direction and beers has now begun to win hearts and minds in the Pennine hinterlands, transforming the brewery's fortunes.

None of the brews featured in the 2017 edition of this book remain on the roster. Current choices include the sessionable pale **Hebden Hop** (3.9%) which derives its piney aromas and fresh fruit flavous from that well-tried hop triumvirate – Citra, Chinook and Cascade. By contrast, Motueka brings bags of gooseberry and apple to the crisp **Haka Pale** (4%), while massive dry hopping with Mosaic, Simcoe and Citra lends tropical fruit weight to the anaemic, unfiltered, unfined **Kalifornia** (4.4%).

Other choices include the smooth and chocolatey oatmeal stout **Cosmonaut** (4.4%) and its stronger, sweeter, porridge-thick, dark chocolate cousin **Supernova** (6.9%). The Exchange Craft Beer House in Bradford is a regular customer, but The Nightjar brewery tap is a reliable place to sample the delights of this re-invented brewery.

Nomadic Beers

Unit 11 Sheepscar House, 15 Sheepscar Street, Leeds, LS7 1AD;
P: 07868 345228; W: nomadicbeers.co.uk; E: info@nomadicbeers.co.uk;
F/T: @nomadicbeers

Just two years after their first brew of Nomadic at Burley Street Brewhouse (see page 37), Katie Marriott and Ross Nicholson have outgrown the brew kit there and moved into a new home across the city in Sheepscar. Their core beers are the best-selling **Pale** (3.8%), modern best bitter **Strider** (4.4%) and juicy American pale **Bandit** (4.8%). These are supported by at least two new specials each month, which have previously included a coffee IPA made with surplus bread and a treacle stout, amongst many others.

The sizeable new site – a real contrast to cramped Burley Street – has allowed them to double capacity to 32 casks per brew and host monthly open taproom events in the brewery, where guests can drink the beer right from the source. Nomadic beers also wander to independent bars in Yorkshire, plus beer festivals across the North of England. Katie and Ross also regularly hit the road to run tap takeover and Meet the Brewer events.

Their single-hopped **Chinook** (4.5%), where the citrus and banana character of the hop is balanced by the pleasantness of the malt, cut nicely through the assault of pie and peas on a recent visit to Foley's tap house in Leeds.

The brewery mural is by Leeds artist Christine Jopling, whose wonderfully imaginative illustrations have featured in beer guides and beer festival programmes published by Leeds CAMRA over many years.

 Freyja (4.9%)

This special is labelled a chocolate cherry stout and it is the first of these flavours which dominates an aroma that hangs over this opaque dark ale as its thin pale head quickly vanishes.

At first encounter its taste is a little disconcerting, but the palate soon acclimatises to its left field attack and unscrambles a luxurious cocktail of flavours – dark chocolate and coffee, woodsmoke and blackberries. By the third mouthful it feels like a much-loved friend and it departs with some warming sweet toffee notes in a perfect finish.

The Nook Brewhouse

Victoria Square, Holmfirth, HD9 2DN; P: 01484 682373;
W: thenookbrewhouse.co.uk; E: office@thenookbrewhouse.co.uk;
F: @thenookbrewhouse; T: @Nookbrewhouse

In 2009 a local brewing tradition was revived in the heart of picturesque Holmfirth with the opening of a brewhouse behind The Rose and Crown pub, where an ancient brewery once stood. A cool cellar built deep below the water line of the neighbouring River Ribble is perfect for conditioning the beer.

Documents and deeds on display in the pub highlight the history of the site and a proud brewing heritage which dates back to 1754. For many of those years, the pub has been known simply as The Nook and for the past two generations has been owned and run by the Roberts family. Ian and Sheila took over in 2000 following the death of their father David and have not only maintained the pub's reputation for great beer, but have expanded the business with the brewery, a bistro, and some top quality bed and breakfast accommodation. Even so, the Nook is proud to have kept a place in the CAMRA Good Beer Guide for more than 35 years.

The brewery produces nearly 5,000 pints a week. Their cask conditioned ales can be found in pubs and bars and at beer festivals across the North of England and beyond; their bottled beers adorned with the grotesque cartoons of the Nook pump clips – each apparently based on some of the pub's regulars – are easy to spot on the supermarket shelves.

Ian and Sheila have recently purchased The Algy Arms (formerly The Bay Horse) at Hade Edge just outside Holmfirth and an extensive refurbishment is under way, including creating more letting bedrooms and changing the layout to make the most of the pub's stunning views of the Pennines. With another busy pub to supply, plans are also being made to extend the site and capacity of the brewhouse itself. A viewing window will allow customers to watch the beer being brewed as they enjoy brewery-fresh beer on the bar.

Regular brews include sessionable, mid-brown – and not especially bitter – **Yorks Bitter** (3.7%), sharp and tangy **Baby Blond** (3.8%), golden and floral **Best** (4.2%) and the full-bodied, slightly treacly **Oat Stout** (5.2%). The list is completed with a good selection of occasional ales and specials.

The brewery recently marked its thousandth brew with the cleverly-named **NOO1K** (7.2%) which developed its complexity – full-bodied with spicy, woody notes and a sweet finish of dried fruit, rum and winter berries – during a long ageing in oak casks. A further celebration beer

and special festival are planned to mark the tenth anniversary of the brewhouse in summer 2019.

Nook'y Brown (4.9%)

You might think that Nook'y Brown is the brewery's own pastiche of the north-eastern favourite – albeit a beer which was long brewed at John Smith's in Tadcaster, and is now brewed in Holland. But at 4.9% ABV the Nook version is a shade stronger than the Geordie beer and perhaps actually a shade or two darker. It has real body and substance, and a mellow, dried fruit, toffeeish taste with some initial zestiness and a lovely warming, bitter finish.

North Brewing

Unit 6, Taverners Walk Industrial Estate, Sheepscar Grove, Leeds, LS7 1AH;
P: 0113 345 3290; W: northbrewing.com; E: sales@northbrewing.com;
F: @northbrewingleeds; T: @northbrewco

North Bar Group was a driving force behind the craft beer movement in Leeds. From its modest beginnings as a small bar in Briggate, the group catalysed a significant change in the city's drinking culture, introducing a public weaned on Tetley's and Sam Smiths to some of the amazing, interesting and occasionally baffling beers available from around the world.

From Briggate, the group built organically, each expansion into new premises keeping roughly in pace with a burgeoning reputation for quality beer, knowledgeable staff and laid-back atmosphere. It was perhaps only a matter of time before North was further seized by the spirit of the times to open its own brewery.

Their first beer, **Session Pale** (3.8%), began life as **Prototype**, initially brewed at Roosters in Knaresborough – and is still the staple choice during my regular visits to the rather lovely Further North in Chapel Allerton.

North Pale (4.1%) pours the kind of hazy yellow which a few years ago might have had you asking the barman to change the barrel, but which has now become the symbol of a beer which hasn't had its life sucked out by filtration. It packs in some of the major fruit experiences which can be derived from Citra and Simcoe hops. The aroma seems sharply acidic, yet on the palate there is more of a sweetness to the taste – all pineapple and tinned peaches – while bitter grapefruit kicks in for a substantial finish.

Though there are some fruity aromatic notes to the pale amber West Coast IPA **Transmission** (6.9%), it's only when it hits the palate that it really starts throwing its weight around. Its strength manifests itself in an immediate blast of big-tasting hops and its full-on bitterness develops into a complex cocktail of grapefruit and passion fruit, almost as though the brew has been spiked with a syrupy concentrate. Curiously for an IPA – whose roots lie in the need for a cooling, refreshing, revitalising beer for the troops – its formidable potency lends some surprising warming qualities. **Herzog** (5%) is a Kolsch; **Pinata** (4.5%) a fresh tropical pale.

The potent **Triple IPA** (10%) was the result of a collaboration with Uiltje Brewery in Haarlem, and when I tried this at Further North, the barman decanted it into the broad bowl of a large brandy glass, whose shape held in so ferocious an aroma of citrus and hop resins that I almost intoxicated myself by breathing its fumes. The smallest sip lathers the tongue with a thick soup of lime, lemon and grapefruit concentrated to vindaloo strength, warming the throat and lulling you towards an etherised unconsciousness. It's as though the Anglo-Dutch brew team would like to congratulate you on choosing a beer from their little collaboration by giving you a big high five. In the face. With a chair. A new brewery tap in Sovereign Street brings these delights to the heart of the city.

🍺 **Full Fathom 5** (6.5%)

It was in North Brewing's original taproom in an industrial unit close to the city centre that I made first acquaintance with this coffee and coconut porter.

Unlike some brews which go down these routes, here neither of those rich flavours is allowed to dominate. Instead, the brewer has created a luscious, jet black, velvety ale which is still essentially a porter, but with enough depth to allow the coffee and the coconut to lend just an influence. At the same time, they contribute to a silky, creamy texture, which perhaps at first serves to disguise its premium strength, though its significant power is finally revealed as it passes down the throat into a long dry aftertaste.

North Riding Brewery

Unit 6, Barkers Lane, Snainton, YO13 9BD; P: 01723 864845;
W: northridingbrewery.com; E: stuart@northridingbrewery.com;
F: @northridingbreweryltd; T: @northridingbrew

Christmas 2018 saw North Riding decamp from East Ayton to Snainton, a few miles further west of Scarborough, where bigger premises offer the opportunity to expand. American hops seem key to Stuart Neilson's recipes with his fruity pale ales **Cascade** (4%), **Citra** (4.5%) and **Mosaic** (4.3%) each named after big-selling varieties. The **US Session** (3.8%) is brewed once monthly with three different US hops each time, while Aussie and New Zealand hops feature in some of the seasonals. Recent additions to Stu's repertoire include the sweet-sounding **Fudge Brownie Stout** (7.4%) and **Dark Rum 'n' Raisin Mild** (4.3%). Scarborough's excellent North Riding Brewpub offers a home to these beers – and plenty more.

North Riding Brewpub

161-163 North Marine Rd, Scarborough, YO12 7HU; P: 01723 370004;
F: @northridingbrewpub; T: @north_riding

Though the small brewkit in the basement of this multi CAMRA award-winning pub is primarily used to provide ale for the pub's customers, its casks do occasionally escape to further afield. I made aquaintance with the lovely, rich and treacly black IPA **Artorias** (7%) in Foley's in Leeds recently. The brewery's patriotic pump clip of a St George's shield makes them easy to spot on any bar.

North Yorkshire Brewing

South Gare Court, Redcar, TS10 5BN; P: 01642 497298;
W: nybrewery.co.uk; E: sales@nybrewery.co.uk; F: @northyorkshirebreweryltd

Though relocating beyond its general pale into Teesside, North Yorkshire Brewing earns a place in this book through its name and its long history as Yorkshire's most northerly brewery.

Leaving Pinchinthorpe Hall after more than 20 years was in any case involuntary, long-time head brewer Razvan Oltianu being forced to move after the hall reverted to being a wedding venue and restaurant. The curiously-named bold and toasty red ale **Read Kjarr** (4%) recalls the ancient name for Redcar, and means "reed marsh".

Premium brown bitter **Flying Herbert** (4.7%) with its tangy bitter marmalade notes remains the flagship product, while pale lager-ale cross **White Lady** (4.7%) recalls a spectre reputed to walk the corridors of Pinchinthorpe, perhaps wondering where the brewery has gone.

Northern Monk

The Old Flax Store, Marshall's Mill, Holbeck, Leeds, LS11 9YJ;
P: 0113 243 6430; W: northernmonk.com;
E: drink@northernmonk.com; F: @northernmonkbrewco; T: @NMBCo

Northern Monk is one of the stellar success stories of British brewing. Just six years after being founded in a cellar in 2013, Northern Monk is now exporting to 23 countries worldwide. The brewery moved into the old flax store of Marshall's Mill in 2014, its utilitarian red brick bulk lending itself beautifully to brewkit, bar and events space.

This success is based on quality, a nod to traditional monastic brewing values – and an ethos of providing crafted, well thought out ales, with a progressive approach to ingredients and techniques.

Heading to the bar you are almost overwhelmed by choice. The back bar has as many lines as a sonnet and each of these fourteen beers has been brewed by Northern Monk.

The core range includes a host of pales – the tangerine-dominated session IPA **Eternal** (4.1%), the gentle and pineapple-accented **Faith** (5.4%) and hazy tropical fruit **Heathen** (7.2%) – to which were added in 2019 the fresh low alcohol **Striding Edge** (2.8%) and gluten-free **Origin** (5.7%). Jet black **Northern Star** (5.9%) is a strong mocha porter – suggestions of dark chocolate and hazelnut and ground coffee beans lend a luxurious decadence which might surprise the London wharf and market porters who once made this style their very own.

It was clever marketing to introduce their bloody Mary porter **Henderson's Relish** (5%) on All Fools' Day – it zipped around the internet with many thinking it a joke, me included. It's a crazy combination, but it works beautifully.

Northern Monk place an emphasis on celebrating the people behind the beers, and each of the rebranded cans features an illustration of one

of the production team. A series of Patrons Projects beers fosters collaboration, creativity and community between artists, athletes and creatives across the north.

The recent expansion into a second brewery south west of the city centre, and the opening of a new Refectory in Manchester's allegedly trendy Northern Quarter are just the

latest chapters in this unfolding story. I have no doubt that such industry would be admired by those who founded Holbeck as one of the workshops of the world. If John Marshall's ghost sometimes eases itself from the brickwork to walk the bare wooden boards of his flax store, I think he might just approve.

New World (6.2%)

Northern Monk's brewing talents stretch from the most low alcohol refreshers to the high-octane piledrivers; at 6.2% this big tasting India Pale Ale comes from somewhere mid-range. The artwork shows a farmer ploughing the soil amid a dramatic landscape of pine forests and vertiginous green-tinged mountains. It also tells us that the first New World hops arrived in Britain in the 1800s – at least a century before I would have thought, and even longer before these new strains began to lend their wonderful characteristics to a host of new craft beers.

Even so, the text is vague about precisely which variety is responsible for the mighty backbone of this cloudy pale ale, which lures the unwary with a pleasant, fruity, flowery aroma – all pineapple and peach – before really throwing its weight around on the palate.

It announces itself on the tongue with some earthy, almost dank bitterness and there is enough of a rich oiliness to the texture to suggest this might be even stronger than its ABV. There are still some juicy, citric notes, but these are fleshed out by the firmer characteristics of pine resins, fresh herbs and even a suggestion of tobacco. As a well-constructed ale it is a perfect example of everything that Northern Monk stands for. But it's not for the faint-hearted.

Old Mill Brewery

Mill Street, Snaith, DN14 9HU; P: 01405 861813; W: oldmillbrewery.co.uk;
E: sales@oldmillbrewery.co.uk; T: @oldmillbrewery

Around 150 years ago, Snaith was well served by brewers and maltsters, though the emergence of the major breweries in nearby Tadcaster saw the trade die out. Only with the opening of Old Mill Brewery in 1983 did this great craft return to a town whose origins lie before the Norman Conquest.

Hundreds attended an open day in 2018 to mark Old Mill's 35th birthday, a celebration which heralded the first shake-up in the brewery's core range for some years, under the stewardship of new head brewer Ryan Truswell. The flagship traditional **Bitter** (3.9%), has now been joined by session IPA **Bullion** (3.7%) and malty, coffee and chocolate porter **La Bolsa** (4.5%). 5p from each pint sold of the Citra-hopped pale ale **12th Man** (4.2%) supports mental health charities – over £1,500 was raised in 2018.

Old Mill supplies its own tied estate of 17 Pubs, as well as free trade in a 50-mile radius. Yorkshire all-rounder Jack Leaning recently joined the brewery as an ambassador.

 Blonde Bombshell (4%)

Pale barley malt, wheat and Czech hops go into producing this almost anaemic beer, another of Old Mill's core range. Once poured it has some suggestions of craft cider, with dry appley aromas before the spicy, clovey elements you might expect of a wheat beer take over on the palate. A little gentle malt emerges in the aftertaste of a beer which delivers at least some of the excitement you might expect a blonde bombshell to provide.

Old Spot Brewery

Manor Farm, Station Road, Cullingworth, Bradford, BD13 5HN;
P: 01535 275566; W: oldspotbrewery.com

Old Spot began brewing in 2005, using kit salvaged from the Boat brewery in Castleford. Brewer Chris Thompson's range includes the coffee and liquorice accented dark mild **Darkside Pup** (3.6%); simple, slightly orangey chestnut bitter **Light But Dark** (4.0%); full-bodied, slightly grassy flaxen ale **OSB** (4.5%) and substantial sweetish porter **Spot O'Bother** (5.5%).

Old Vault Brewery

12 Market Place, Thorne, Doncaster, DN8 5DP;
P: 01405 947180; F: @theoldvaultthorne

The local CAMRA branch reports that equipment problems have brought a temporary halt to brewing at this popular pub, which may explain their lack of response to my polite inquiries. Hopefully both will be rectified soon.

On The Edge Brewery

Woodseats, Sheffield; P: 07854 983197; W: ontheedgebrew.com;
E: ontheedgebrew@gmail.com; T: ontheedgebrew

Thomas Richards and Luisa Golob operate a tiny brewing plant in their kitchen. No brew is the same as the last and the beers go to pubs such as The Broadfield, Abbeydale Road and the interesting Mallard on Worksop station. A string of awards from local festivals – including a runner-up prize in CAMRA's 2012 Beer of Sheffield contest – underline the quality from this most micro of microbreweries.

Ossett Brewery

Low Mill Road, Ossett, WF5 8ND; T: 01924 261333;
W: www.ossett-brewery.co.uk; E: brewery@ossett-brewery.co.uk;
F/T: @ossettbrewery

Over 20 years of steady growth has seen Ossett build from a microbrewery into one of the region's major players with 27 pubs, nationwide distribution, and with three craft breweries – Rat, Fernandes and Riverhead – added to the fold.

The success is founded on four solidly performing real ales: easy-drinking traditional bitter **Yorkshire Brunette** (3.7%), amiable, malty **Yorkshire Blonde** (3.9%), multi-award-winning crisp, dry **Silver King** (4.3%) and premium pale ale **Excelsior** (5.2%).

Seasonal and limited edition ales extend the choice still further. Ossett's excellent chain of Hop pubs – and bars such as Archie's and Craft Asylum in Leeds are the ideal places to immerse yourself in the whole Ossett experience. A visit to the Hop in Leeds, set into the brooding Dark Arches, where water rushes beneath and trains rumble overhead, is a chance to marvel at the ingenuity of Industrial Revolution engineering.

Treacle Stout (5%)

The addition of dark treacle adds depth, substance and some real sweetness to Ossett's interpretation of this ancient brewing style. The label's teaspoon dripping glistening black gloop leaves you in no doubt what to expect. And though its influence isn't so apparent on the nose, as soon as this beer crosses the threshold, the treacle asserts itself, lending a smooth lathering of warmth and sweetness across the palate. There are some nice vanilla notes in there too and a tender, dusty dry finish, tempting you to open another.

Outgang Brewery

Kinsley Hotel, Wakefield Road, Kinsley, WF9 5EH;
P: 07747 694611; E: thebrew@sky.com

The time was, before a vindictive Government ripped the heart from its communities, that parts of Yorkshire thrived on coal. Some of mining's folklore is preserved in the names of the traditional ales produced by Outgang in Kinsley, whose drift mine closed in 1986, shortly after the end of the miners' strike. **Lamp Room** (3.9%) is a lemony blonde, **Tailgate Ripper** (3.9%) an amber Yorkshire best bitter, **Pit Bottom** (4%) a malty ale of substantial darkness and body and just a hint of vanilla.

Kinsley Hotel landlord Gordon Mair has an album of pictures from the time of the Kinsley Evictions, when miners were forced out of their homes amid a dispute with the colliery management. This was 1905, presaging the ravages of Thatcher by eighty years.

Outhouse Brewing

Unit 16a, Redbrook Business Park, Wilthorpe Road, Barnsley, S75 1JN;
P: 07572 164446; W: outhousebrewing.co.uk;
E: info@outhousebrewing.co.uk; F/T; @outhousebrewing

With his beers named after the people they were designed for, newcomer Andy Jones's beer roster reads like the back four of a Sunday league football team. There's pale **Ollie** (4.1%), sessionable **Henry** (4.3%), stout **Edd** (4.5%) and **Ged** (3.8%), who is not only pale but has been certified as gluten free.

All are produced on the Jolly Boys Brewery kit – and have started to make their way into pubs such as The Jolly Tap in Wakefield and The Crown at Elsecar.

Partners Brewery

589 Halifax Road, Hightown, Liversedge, WF15 8HQ;
P: 01924 457772; E: sales@partnersbrewery.co.uk

Mungo and shoddy were once products of the heavy woollen district, cloth made from recycling rags and scraps of material. Partners has recycled the dyehouse of the Henry Day Mungo and Shoddy Mill into a brewhouse and bar and established a solid local reputation for ales like the crisp **Blonde** (3.9%), the not overly-hoppy but more mainstream **American Craft Ale** (4.5%) and – best of all – gloriously hoppy, fruity, wheat-beer influenced **Tabatha** (6%). In 2016, Partners absorbed Ossett's Bob's Brewery into their operation, bringing the light and flowery **White Lion** (4.3%) – and other colours of Lion – into the portfolio. Partners in turn passed into the ownership of Mill Valley brewery in 2019.

Penistone Brewers

The White Heart, Bridge Street, Penistone, S36 7AH; P: 01226 762843;
W: thewhiteheart.co.uk; F: @thewhiteheart.co.uk; T: @thewhiteheart36

The White Heart traces its history back to 1377, when beer was being brewed on the premises. This tradition was revived in 2017, and though they can sometimes be found elsewhere, the pub remains the ideal place to sample the four cask ales from their microbrewery. They are the robust porter **Back Oil Tap** (4.9%), gluten-free premium bitter **Amber's Brew** (4.3%), Belgian-style **Blonde Bombshell** (4.7%) and crisp honeyed **Queen Bee** (4.7%).

Pennine Brewing Co

Well Hall Farm, Bedale, DL8 2PX; P: 01677 470111;
W: pennine-brewing.co.uk; E: info@pennine-brewing.co.uk;
F: @penninebrewingco; T: @penninebrewery

Pennine decamped in 2013 from Batley in 2013 to the edge of the rolling Vale of Mowbray, a bucolic stretch of low-lying land between the North York Moors and the Hambleton Hills to the east and the Yorkshire Dales to the west. A dizzying and dazzling domain of special and seasonal ales means they have always got something different to offer to augment a core roster: the mellow, creamy and easy-going **Best Bitter** (3.9%), hoppy **Natural Gold** (4.2%), significantly fruity **Real Blonde** (4%), and the sparkling **Amber Necker** (3.8%). Attractive ruby session ale **Northland** (4.1%) is a well-balanced ale of dark fruit and toffee aromas, whose significant sharp, hoppy character emerges in the last knockings but Pennine's standout performer is the blonde and caramelly **Hair of the Dog** (3.9%) which has garnered a string of awards and is a "must-have" beer wherever you find it.

🍺 Pennine Millie George (4%)

Styled as a "blonde with attitude", this is named after the daughter of the brewers; bright and highly-carbonated, it looks for all the world like Lucozade, glimmering attractively in the glass. It is very much aimed at the sessionable end of the market, tripping across the palate with a delicate, thirst-quenching, easy-going nature. That buzzy, almost fizzy appearance yields some bready notes in the aroma; on the palate it has a friendly, only faintly hoppy nature, with just a little bitterness in the finish. In this companionable character it never quite manages to throw off the impression of being just like Lucozade, a perfect reviving tonic for the thirsty.

Premium Beverage Refreshments

120 Mangham Road, Rotherham, S62 6EF

Two varieties of **Freddies Fruit Lager** (4%) – one with mango and one with wild berries – are apparently produced by this South Yorkshire brewery, though they seem rather hard to track down.

Quirky Ales

Ash Lane, Garforth, Leeds, LS25 2ET; P: 0113 286 2072; W: quirkyales.com; E: info@quirkyales.com; F/T: @quirkyales

On an industrial estate on the edge of Garforth, hidden away behind low-rise workshops and warehouses, something remarkable is taking place. Led by a former police firearms commander, this brewhouse and bar is drawing a regular following to this most unpromising of locations.

It's the brainchild of Mike Quirk who began home brewing in 2015 after handing in his warrant card and looking for something less stressful to do with his time. It soon evolved from the quaint and quirky to the quite extraordinary as Mike upgraded his tiny brewkit to some serious stainless steel and installed it at this unprepossessing warehouse, just outside the centre of Garforth, where regular guest brew days give all-comers the

chance to try their hand at making a beer.

The taproom next door has just a handful of tables, while other drinkers stand or lean on the bar, or admire the impressive line-up of bottled beers on sale. It's open from Thursday to Sunday, and it must have taken quite a leap of faith to believe that drinkers would come here, but they do. They even manage to shoehorn live acts onto an impromptu stage beside the door, though accommodating anyone bigger than a duo wouldn't leave room for their equipment. Or an audience.

The Tap has a very friendly atmosphere and a log burning stove that makes it very popular with ramblers and dog walkers.

Mike brews three times a week, and the choice on draught varies from day to day. They include New Zealand pale **Two Islands** (3.8%) and the more contemporary IPA **Hip Hop** (5.5%). The pick of the bunch for me is the impressively substantial, rich red brown **Classic** (5.7%), packed with

the sweetness of dark fruit and bonfire toffee and undoubtedly a homage to Theakston's Old Peculier.

An ever-increasing number of pubs, clubs and restaurants regularly take Quirky casks, while beer festival crowds across the region have been quick to warm to Mike's ales, which are also available in bottle. The brewery has recently been listed as one of the top 10 breweries to visit in Yorkshire and rates a mention in the Lonely Planet Guide.

Garforth Porter (4.8%)

Garforth Porter sounds like a seven-foot-tall West Indian fast bowler, happy of nature, deadly of intent. Quirky was the nickname he acquired as a rangy 12-year-old on the school playing field as he heaved down steepling bouncers at unsuspecting sixth-formers.

Once poured, this beer looks a formidable sight, jet black with a foaming beige head and some enticing liquorice aromas. But once on the palate it's a much more benign proposition, surprisingly soft and blessedly meek with a hint of malt. It trips lightly across the tongue, almost insubstantial and very refreshing and drinkable. It's almost 5% ABV, but you wouldn't guess it was this premium strength. Only in the finish does some true quirky character emerge as you're hit with a late blast of blackberries and dusty old books.

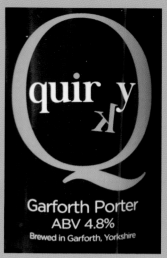

Garforth Porter
ABV 4.8%
Brewed in Garforth, Yorkshire

Rat Brewery

40 Chapel Hill, Huddersfield, HD1 3EB;
P: 01484 542400; E: ratcrafted@rat-brewery.co.uk;
F/T: @ratbrewery

The Rat and Ratchet was established as a brewpub in 1994, and though brewing ceased for several years it began again in 2011, following the pub's purchase by Ossett Brewery. Brewer Paul Spencer describes himself as Head Rodent – and he clearly has a penchant for puns, with beers such as the uber-hopped IPA **Rat Against the Machine** (7%), **Imperial Stout Ratsputin** (7.4%) and bottled barley wine **Grapes Of Rat** (10%). Regular products include pale and bitter **White Rat** (4%), dark coffee-ish porter **Black Rat** (4.5%) and the straw-coloured, wine-nosed, New Zealand-hopped **King Rat** (5%) – with beers available in cask and keg.

Raven Hill Brewery

Raven Hill Farm, Driffield, YO25 4EG; P: 07979 674573;
W: ravenhillbrewery.com; E: hello@ravenhillbrewery.com;
F: @ravenhillbrewery; T: @ravenhillbrew

These newcomers are already making a name for their bottle-conditioned ales, brewed on a farm in the rolling pastures north of Driffield. Many of the beers take their name from the local geography: roasted malts and flaked oats lend weight and substance to **Ridge Way** (5.5%), there's a crisp and refreshing nature to the light pale **Chalk Stream** (4%), while dry-hopping with Amarillo adds freshness to the aroma of the pale ale **Brook** (4.3%).

 **Saison** (5%)

Traditional Belgian Saisons would be laid down for maturation in cellars for drinking later in the year, typically to slake the thirst of hardworking farmhands during the harvest. The characteristic dank sourness you would expect of that naturally-fermented style is evident from the moment you open this pale, slightly hazy golden ale with its exuberant head. The palate soon acclimatises to this bitter attack, revealing delightful cherry and blueberry peeping out from behind the sour.

Recoil Brewing

Lee Mills, St Pauls Rd, Keighley, BD21 4QW; P: 01756 243243;
W: copperdragon.co.uk; E: info@recoilbrewing.co.uk;
F: @copperdragonbrewery; T: @news_copper

For a while, Recoil operated as an independent brewery as battle raged over the future of Copper Dragon. "We didn't know how long it was going to take, so this was our contingency," explains production manager Matthew Taylor. Though Copper Dragon's future is now settled, Recoil beers such as the firmly bitter but sessionable **Blonde Avenger** (3.9%) and the amber **Back to Best** (3.8%) will continue to find their way to market.

Regather

57-59 Club Garden Road, Sheffield, S11 8BU; P: 0114 273 1258;
W: www.regather.net; E: info@regather.net; F: @regather; T: @regatherworks

The Regather Co-Operative is based in the historic Horn Handle Works in Sharrow, just south of Sheffield city centre, where a brewery producing unfined and unfiltered beers sits alongside an events venue and organic vegetable business.

Beyond the regular **Pale Ale** (4.8%) and **IPA** (5.3%), both of which are big favourites in the Regather bar, the 150-litre craft brewery produces interesting, well thought out, cosmopolitan-influenced bottled ales. **Achtzig Deutsche Mark Bitte** (5.2%) is a dark, malty, Scottish 80-shilling brewed with German and Vienna malts; **Winter Solstice** (5.6%) is a crisp, dry, full-flavoured IPA given a sharp grapefruit finish by Mandarina Bavaria hops. **Edelreiss** (5.7%) is a complex German Weissbier, slightly darker than you would expect, with distinctive bubblegum and banana flavours; uber-hopped citrus-heavy **Sheffield Nevada** (5.6%) is a tribute to the classic Sierra Nevada pale. Regather offers Brew Day experiences for customers to design a beer and help with the brewing process – an ideal Christmas or birthday present.

Undergoing something of a hiatus as we went to press, brewing should have re-started by the time you read this.

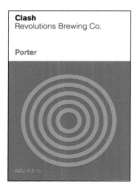

Clash
Revolutions Brewing Co.

Porter

ABV 4.5 %

Manifesto
Revolutions Brewing Co.

Stout

ABV 6.0 %

Swoon
Revolutions Brewing Co.

Chocolate Fudge
Milk Stout

ABV 4.5 %

Revolutions Brewing

Unit B7, Whitwood Enterprise Park,
Castleford, WF10 5PX;
P: 01977 552649;
W: revolutionsbrewing.co.uk;
E: mark@revolutionsbrewing.co.uk;
F: @revolutionsbrewing;
T: @revolutionsbrew

Now pushing towards its tenth birthday, the Castleford brewer has gained a strong reputation for a great range of interesting beers, several of which draw upon musical inspiration.

The core range also includes the sessionable pale ale **Candidate** (3.9%), the rotating hop pale ale **Switch** (4.5%), big-bodied London porter **Clash** (4.5%), the US IPA **Marquee** (5.4%) and **Manifesto Stout** (6.0%).

Revolutions has recently begun an on-going collaborative partnership with Henry Smith Brewery to showcase more traditional beer styles – Henry Smith **Best Bitter**, **Blonde**, **Session IPA** and **Dark Mild** (all 4.0%). Each is made only with locally-sourced malt, English hops and contains a signature dash of oats in the grist for extra smoothness and body.

 Swoon (4.5%)

Initially intended as a one-off brew in 2017, this chocolate milk fudge stout took gold at the SIBA regional awards in 2017, followed by seven "beer of the festival" prizes – and has become the flagship beer of a brewery where sales have risen 20% year on year. Fudge dominates the taste, but there are hints of raisins, chocolate and plenty more of a sweetshop nature to a beer which is proving a little local phenomenon.

Richmond Brewing Company

The Old Station, Richmond, DL10 4LD; P: 01748 828266;
W: richmondbrewing.co.uk; E: enquiries@richmondbrewing.co.uk;
F: @richmondbrewingcompany; T: @richmondbrewing

In 2016, new fermenting and conditioning tanks and a bar for visitors to sample the beers doubled the size of the brewery based in Richmond's stunning riverside Victorian railway station which closed to trains in 1969 and is now home to cinemas, galleries and a number of artisan food producers.

Deep brown ale **Swale** (3.7%) divides opinion, according to boss Chris Wallace who adds: "But CAMRA go mad for it." It has some surprising vinegar sharpness on the nose which might easily fool you into thinking this might be a sour Belgian fruit beer. Yet on the palate that soon disappears behind a blanket of malt and toffee, that develops some genuine bitterness as it fades away. Beers of this very moderate strength rarely deliver quite so much. Other beers include the light and golden **Station Ale** (4%), and the dark malty **Drummer Boy** (3.8%).

Stump Cross (4.7%)

The bones of reindeer, bison and wolverines have been found in the four miles of Stump Cross Caverns between Pateley Bridge and Grassington, discovered by lead miners in the 19th century and believed to date back almost half a million years. Natural cave water, filtered through the limestone, is added to this premium bitter which pours a rich deep red, with a tight foaming head and some notable suggestions of toffee in the aroma. On the palate, Stump Cross develops some sweetish fruitcakey tastes of cherry and marzipan, with a significant malt presence that trumps any bitter influence from the hops.

Ridgeside Brewery

Unit 24, Penraevon 2 Industrial Estate, Jackson Road, Leeds LS7 2AW;
P: 07595 380568; W: ridgesidebrewery.co.uk;
E: accounts@ridgesidebrewery.co.uk;
F/T: @ridgesidebrewer

The sad death of Simon Bolderson in 2014 robbed Leeds brewing of a legend. Over just four years, this big-hearted bear of a man had established Ridgeside's reputation for craft ales which were a guarantee of quality on bars around the city – not least at nearby East of Arcadia, the first to give him a permanent place on the bar.

Thankfully the Ridgeside story continues, underpinned by the recent purchase of new fermenters to increase capacity. Pale **Cascadia** (4.1%) is driven by the spice and citrus characteristics of the Cascade hop; US and European hops are blended into the more robust **Baja** (5.5%). A host of other beers are available in cask, keg and can. Their greatest tribute to Simon is that two of his characteristic traditional British beers – and rock-themed names – are maintained: the easy-going session pale **Jailbreak** (4%) and fulsome sweetish oatmeal stout **Black Night** (5%).

Riverhead Brewery

2 Peel Street, Marsden, Huddersfield, HD7 6BR; P: 01484 844324;
W: theriverheadmarsden.co.uk; E: brewery@ossett-brewery.co.uk;
F: @riverheadbrewerytap; T: @RiverheadBrewer

Though now owned by regional heavyweight Ossett Brewery, Riverhead remains a tiny two-barrel plant whose production goes largely to the brewery tap above. Here Richard Armitage produces a catalogue of seasonal beers infused with locally-sourced fruits and herbs such as **Sherbert Lemon** (4.1%) and **Sour Cherry Red** (3.9%). These are in addition to his reservoir-themed regular beers, the soothing, under-stated, lightly fruity **Butterley Bitter** (3.8%), the more assertively caramel and biscuity **March Haigh** (4.6%) and the full-bodied **Redbrook Premium** (5.5%).

Rooster's Brewing Co.

Unit H5, Fifth Avenue, Hornbeam Park, Harrogate, HG2 8QT;
T: 01423 865959; W: roosters.co.uk;
E: hello@roosters.co.uk;
F: @roostersbrewing; T: @roostersbrewco

Years from now, when someone traces the bloodline of the craft beer revolution, they will find Rooster's writ large in the DNA. Brewer Sean Franklin embraced the new hop varieties emerging in America's Yakima Valley, and put them front centre in a series of elegant, crisp, juicy pale ales. It's not stretching a point too far to say that the sparkling spicy, floral, **Yankee** (4.3%) is a beer that turned the British brewing scene on its head. Now, it's a modern classic and relatively tame compared to some weightily-hopped newcomers, but they owe much to its bravery and ultimately its success. Still the brewery's flagship ale, it continues to pick up prizes, including a gold award at the 2019 SIBA National Independent Beer Awards.

Sean retired in 2011, and worked alongside twins Oliver and Tom

Fozard to ensure a smooth transition to the new owners. Though they have substantially expanded the range, and invested heavily in increasing capacity – latterly relocating to a new home in Hornbeam Park in Harrogate, with an on-site taproom – their beers remain true to Sean's legacy.

Rooster's core range of beers includes the floral, slightly sweet, grassy **YPA** (4.1%), **24/7** (4.7%) a session IPA that derives complex fruit character from a cocktail of American Amarillo, Simcoe and Chinook hops – plus fashionable New Zealander Nelson Sauvin. The selection extends yet further across different styles of beer and is supplemented by a range of limited edition beers brewed on a rotational basis. The thin, inconsequential, watermelon pale ale **Scrambler** (4%) is a rare mis-step in this brewery's sure-footed progress.

Baby-Faced Assassin (6.1%)

Rooster's reputation as a trendsetter didn't end with their enthusiastic adoption of American hops. In 2015 the brewery installed a micro-canning plant in their Knaresborough Brewery and started putting some of their award-winning beers into cans, a move once derided by the purists. There's a really enticing tropical fruit blast to the aroma of Baby-Faced Assassin, one of the first three Rooster's beers given the aluminium treatment. This continues into a complex taste, heavy with mango and oranges, but so delightfully easy drinking that its placid nature offers a false sense of security. Only when you read its strength in the small print do you realise the dangerous nature of this aptly-named assassin.

The new Rooster's brewery in Hornbeam Park, Harrogate includes this impressive new taproom.

Rudgate Brewery

2 Centre Park, Marston Business Park, Tockwith, YO26 7QF;
P: 01423 358382; W: rudgatebrewery.co.uk;
E: sales@rudgatebrewery.co.uk; T/F: @rudgatebrewery

There's a whole heap of history here, from the Romans to the RAF. Marston Moor was the site of a pivotal civil war battle; 300 years later it was the wartime base for Halifax Bombers. In my youth, Tockwith was synonymous with learning to drive. The old airfield there remains a place where learners can get behind the wheel, sure in the knowledge that there's nothing to crash into other than long grass, traffic cones and, er, other learners.

Established in 1992 in the airfield's former ammunition store, the brewery is named after the old Roman road which crossed the Vale of York.

Ruby Mild (4.4%) has some liquorice and toffee on the nose, then a big blast of ripe fruits on the palate, followed by a surge of unexpected late bitterness. The dark amber best bitter **Battle Axe** (4.2%) may lack the full-on thunderous potency suggested by the name, but has bags of damsonny, fruitloafy malt in the aroma and some nice caramel sweetness to the taste. **Valkyrie** (5%) is a nicely-constructed American pale ale, bursting with oranges and is again rather sweeter and more benign than its Wagnerian name suggests.

Rudgate love to freshen up their range with a cornucopia of seasonals, occasionals and specials – the current list runs to four pages.

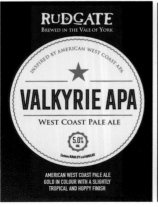

🍺 **Jorvik** (4.6%)

Jorvik, of course, is the Viking name for York, though it's unlikely the Scandinavian invaders had anything quite like this to drink. Styled a flaxen blonde ale, this attractive golden beer with its prickly gingerish aroma is wonderfully refreshing, yet packed with the kind of fruit and marzipan flavours usually associated with darker, stronger, winter warmers. And the truth is, if those Viking hordes had come across this stuff – or the slightly less potent cask version – they might have calmed down a bit and concentrated more on the simple pleasures of getting gently sozzled in like-minded company, rather than that whole strenuous and no doubt tiresome business of war, rape and pillage.

Ryedale Brewing

Roseberry, Moor Lane, Sinnington, York, YO62 6SE;
P: 01751 433229; W: ryedalebrewing.co.uk; E: info@ryedalebrewing.co.uk;
F: @ryedalebrewing

After a spell brewing in Keighley, brothers David and Tony Williams are now back where they started in Ryedale – though issues in finding new premises have caused a frustrating year-long hiatus, with their equipment mothballed in the garage. "It's been a rough 12 months," says Tony. Plans to move along the A170 to Allerston fell through, but now they are hopeful of setting up in Sinnington by autumn 2019 – which will see a welcome return for their core range of beers, including the pale golden **Angler** (3.8%), quintessential dark Yorkshire bitter **Rambler** (3.8%), and Chinook-driven **Ryedale Harvest** (3.8%). Bottle-conditioning their brews could open a whole new market in the coming months.

Salt Beer Factory

199 Bingley Road, Saltaire, BD18 4DH;
W: saltbeerfactory.co.uk;
E: sales@saltbeerfactory.co.uk;
F/T: @saltbeerfactory

Mill owner Sir Titus Salt was reputedly teetotal. No pubs were allowed in the village he built for his workers, his dedication to a fervent non-conformism embodied in the beautiful canalside church opposite his mill, and where, incidentally, my dad was minister in the 1990s.

Whether the great philanthropist will be turning in his mausoleum at the village's latest brewery is open to question, but his high-minded non-conformist principles have long since been subsumed beneath a welter of fine public houses, notably Fanny's Alehouse a short walk from the cobbled side streets of this UNESCO village.

The latest addition to the Ossett family of breweries, Salt began with the simple dream of brewing great craft lager, but its scope evolved into something much greater. Visit now to experience its growing range, which includes a sliding scale of IPAs: moderately bitter thirst-quencher **Jute** (4.2%), the more aggressively-hopped **Huckaback** (5.5%), dry-hopped and intensely tropical **Alpaca** (6.6%) and the intense, double dry-hopped, double IPA **Ikat** (8%).

The taproom of this former tramshed features live music, and woodfired pizzas. A changing choice of stouts, lagers and brewing collaborations freshen the beer menu, though with a name like this it's surely only a matter of time until they produce a Gose.

Saltaire Brewery

Dockfield Road, Shipley, Bradford, BD17 7AR; P: 01274 594959;
W: saltairebrewery.com; E: info@saltairebrewery.co.uk; F/T: @saltairebrewery

"We practically had to prise people's fingers from the image of the mill," says boss Ewen Gordon, discussing Saltaire Brewery's recent change of branding. The removal of Sir Titus Salt's great mill from their bottles and pump clips reveals an elegant distancing of themselves from the village: "We have a great reputation nationally and overseas," says Ewen. "Our beers go to 68 countries. Some drinkers know the village and its history, but for a lot of people Saltaire is simply the name of the brewery."

Based in an old generating station which once supplied the electricity

for Bradford's trams, Saltaire has established itself as a regional powerhouse since brewing began a decade ago. The design of their simple new SB logo echoes the local street signs and the shallow sloping gable end of the tramshed's roofline: "It's a more usable icon and it's about building our own identity," he says.

Among beers to be relaunched with the new-look branding is the very pale **Saltaire Blonde** (4%) which has some interesting sweet malty characteristics to balance its significant hoppy nature. Nelson Sauvin hops from New Zealand exert a muscular fruity influence to belie the moderate strength of **South Island** (3.5%), while the punchy, pithy **Cascade** (4.8%) features the bitter talents of the ubiquitous American hop.

The traditional bitter **Titus** (3.9%) – formerly popular Saltaire Pride – pours an attractive sunshine colour with a firm and persistent creamy head that perhaps masks some of the aroma. But it really asserts itself on the palate, an insistent dry and grapefruity bitterness zings across the tongue, aided by some refreshing effervescence.

There's a proper whiff of dandelion and burdock when you prise the cap from a bottle of the so-called Black IPA **Polarity** (6.2%) re-badged from its previous name, Kala. I say "so-called", because there is still a significant body of opinion which would justifiably assert that an India Pale Ale can only be pale, and certainly not black. But from the Big Bang of Jaipur and the American east coast, the whole universe of IPA has expanded exponentially and there is little sign of a deceleration. It is now a badge that all brewers must apply to at least one of their beers,

however little they happen to resemble the original heavily-hopped ales once exported to slake the thirsts of the soldiers of the Raj.

This rich and substantial, oily jet black ale, with toffee, caramel and liquorice to the forefront, is more of a strong firm porter for me, than anything with the refreshing bitter bite of a traditional IPA. It delivers plenty of firm autumnal, woody flavour, turbocharged by a significant hit of carbonation with some surprising sweetness lurking enticingly to the rear.

🍺 **Triple Choc** (4.8%)

The colour scheme used for this luxurious, indulgent stout echoes that of Cadbury's, as though the purple might elicit a Pavlovian response. It takes only a small shift in the balance of malts to effect a significant change of colour; here just 10% of chocolate malt is sufficient to ensure

this beer emerges a seemingly impenetrable black. Only as you hold the glass to the light do you discern a little dazzle of ruby red. Its pale head clings with determination to the side of the glass as the level falls. There are some heady spirit-like influences on the nose, almost as though you have poured yourself a Bailey's, and it shares some of the liqueur's indulgent creamy character on the palate. Some coffee and orange bitterness prevent the chocolate from dominating.

Samuel Smith's Brewery

The Old Brewery, High Street, Tadcaster, North Yorkshire, LS24 9SB;
P: 01937 832225; W: samuelsmithsbrewery.co.uk;
F: @samuelsmithsbrewery; T: @samsmithsbeer

Fiercely, determinedly – sometimes maddeningly – traditional, Yorkshire's oldest brewery continues to plough its own distinctive furrow. The beers are brewed with water from the 85-foot well sunk in 1758, fermented in slate squares with the same strain of yeast they used in Victorian times, and delivered to their vast estate of pubs in wooden casks. When you

step into one, whether in the north where there are many, or in London where there are several rather splendid ones, you are guaranteed only to find their own products – beers, wines, spirits, pop. Don't bother asking for the guest beer because they won't have one.

Head instead for the creamy and malty **Old Brewery Bitter** (4%), the lighter but dryer, hoppier **Best Bitter** (3.7%) or the robust caramelly **Dark Mild** (2.8%) whose bags of taste belie its shandy-level strength.

It's worth exploring their bottles too. Their fruit beers – Organic Cherry, Strawberry and Raspberry – are, like the idiosyncratic company itself, something of an oddity in brewing terms. Quite unlike the tart lambics of Belgian extraction, these soft and refreshing ales start life in Lincolnshire, where the ancient, time-warped All Saint's Brewery in Stamford

produces a lovely handcrafted ale, which is shipped up the Great North Road to Tadcaster, where Sam Smith's blend this with organic fruit juice. **Organic Raspberry** (5.1%) is a surprising translucent red with a firm pink head, and the sweet aroma of fruit cordial; although the raspberries remain in evidence in the taste, they are never over-dominant.

During a year-long maturation in oak casks, **Yorkshire Stingo** (8%) develops the smooth, rounded dried

fruit and liquorice flavours which deftly disguise its strength. It delivers a rich and unexpected blast of treacle as soon as it splashes across the tongue. Only in a long and genuinely warming aftertaste do you get a sense of its true potency.

A recent development saw Sam Smith's pubs ban mobile phones and laptops too – which is great if you are trying to encourage conversation, less so for those who like to sit with a pint while doing some work. You know, beer writers, that kind of thing.

 ## Winter Welcome (6%)

This sturdy seasonal ale comes in 550ml bottles, a characteristically curious measure, a drip short of an American pint and a splash short of an Imperial one. The label looks like something from the Great War, but the design and recipe change every year.

Lacking genuine imagination, I always expect a winter beer to be dark, syrupy and packed with sweet Christmas cake richness, cinnamon and spice. This one (actually the 2016-17 vintage) is bright and gold with a foaming head and some honey notes in the aroma. With a heady dose of soporific malty warmth in there to drive out the winter chill, the taste is a deal more interesting than some Christmas craft ales with funky elves on the label, rather than this cracker-pulling Edwardian couple in their woolly jumpers. Instead, this seems a high-octane take on regular Sam Smith's Bitter – richer, maltier, more potent, and perhaps with some hints of brandy in the finish and a dry orangey aftertaste – its beautiful simplicity emblematic of everything Tadcaster's wonderful, quirky, infuriating Old Brewery has been doing for generations.

Scarborough Brewery

Barry's Lane, Scarborough, YO12 4HA; P: 01723 367506;
W: scarboroughbrewery.co.uk; E: scarboroughbrews@gmail.com;
F: @scarboroughbrewery

2019 marks the tenth birthday of a brewery whose scallop shell logo and maritime beer names celebrate the resort's symbiosis with the sea. Lemon and passion fruit dominate the sessionable **Trident** (3.8%) and there is a significant fruity edge to the American-hopped golden ales **Sealord** (4.3%) and **Ship of Fools** (4.5%) which is given full voice in the toffee-and-tropical **Old Sailor** (4.9%).

There are some curious, perhaps slightly off-putting aromas to **Citra** (4.2%) but once on the palate its invigorating lemony flavours emerge, while a muscular **Stout** (4.6%) shifts the emphasis into coffee, chocolate, smoke, toast and prunes. Though of moderate strength, **Transmission** (3.9%) with its hoppy aroma and subtle citrus flavours is a perfect introduction to the range.

Shadow Brewing

44 Whiteley Croft Rise, Otley, LS21 3NR; P: 07792 690536;
W: www.shadowbrewing.co.uk; E: hello@shadowbrewing.co.uk;
T: @shadow_brewing

Having bought the bulk of his equipment from Wilde Child as Keir upgraded his own burgeoning operation, Ian Shutt was still assembling his one-barrel brewkit as this book went to press. Even so, working with other brewers has allowed him to create his first beer, the full-blooded **Spectre IPA** (5.8%), while a collaboration with fellow-newbies Horsforth Brewing was set to be unveiled at the Leeds CAMRA beer festival. An as-yet-unnamed 4% American Pale is due to be the next to emerge from the Shadow.

Settle Brewery

Unit 2B, The Sidings Industrial Estate, Settle, BD24 9RP;
P: 01729 824936; W: settlebrewery.co.uk; E: hops@settlebrewery.co.uk;
F: @SettleBrewingCompany; T: @settlebrewery

The Settle-Carlisle line offers one of the most spectacular rail journeys in Britain. From the sidings close to Settle station, the town's brewery is providing some similarly dazzling sensory experiences. Its flagship craft products are the well-balanced and sessionable **Blonde** (3.6%) and the traditional Yorkshire ale **Mainline** (3.8%) whose energetic hop quality is balanced by some moderate dark fruit sweetness.

Nº4
NINE STANDARDS
AMBER ALE

A RICH MALTY AMBER ALE WITH
FRAGRANT HOPS, HINTS OF CITRUS
AND A SPICY NOSE

ABV 3.7%

CRAFT ALES BY SETTLE BREWERY

Yet beyond these fiercely traditional ales and their 'age of steam' pump clips, Settle has stretched into the craft market with beers marketed under the Just The Ticket and Nine Standards labels – the latter formerly brewed in Cumbria. **Attermire** (4.2%) is a proper juicy, citric IPA yet brewed to a mundane, sessionable strength; **Nine Standards Porter** (4.7%) is a jet black, creamy, smoky, coffee, caramel delight. A host of monthly specials includes the American-influenced **Blood Orange IPA** (4.8%), and the creamy, coffee-ish **Ernie's Milk Stout** (4.5%).

Sheffield Brewery

J C Albyn Complex, Burton Road, Sheffield, S3 8BT; P: 0114 272 7256;
W: sheffieldbrewery.com; E: sales@sheffieldbrewery.com;
F: @sheffieldbrewery; T: @sheffieldbrewer

Joseph Pickering's Victorian silver polish business was symbiotic with Sheffield's burgeoning cutlery and silver plate industries. It expanded into furniture polish – then cornered the market with Blanco, a white polish used by the military for webbing, khaki and helmets and by tennis and cricket players for their shoes and pads. Though the business finally closed in the 1960s, its echoes can still be felt in Sheffield Brewery, which now uses Pickering's abandoned factory premises. A little museum in the basement is a shrine to shine.

When the brewery moved in here in 2006, it had lain virtually undisturbed for 40 years, and I suspect that old Joseph would recognise something of himself in the industry of head brewer Dr Tim Stillman, who left a 25-year career in academe to turn his biochemistry to productive use: "I was in X-ray crystallography research and I enjoyed it, but there was always the pressure of having to apply for research grants."

And though his research now largely involves hops and malt, Tim says there are some important cross-overs between this and his former life. "There's a lot of science to this. You need exactly the right temperature and timing for the enzymes to go to work in the brew. Things can go wrong very quickly."

His core beers are right in the brewing mainstream. The first two he introduced were named after the city's defining geographical features – light, bright and easy-going pale ale **Five Rivers** (3.8%) and the drier, hoppier and more determinedly bitter **Seven Hills** (4.1%). There's some nutty, caramelly goodness to the traditional Yorkshire bitter **Crucible Best** (3.8%) while there's a dark, silky, chocolate and coffee complexity to **Sheffield Porter** (4.4%) which belies its moderate strength. With its

Czech hops and lager malt, **Blanco Blonde** (4.2%) is an ale in name only.

Each September Tim welcomes students to the city with a new edition of his **Fresh Start** pale ale (4.5%), and has spread his wings into some whimsical specials such as the 'raspberry wheat ice cream pale ale' **Sunburn** (5.2%) and the breakfast stout **Berlin Black** (5.7%) to which smoked malt lends a sausage twist to a morning feast of oats, wheat and lactose.

Some of Tim's beers make their way into bottles; a taproom cheek-by-jowl with the brewhouse allows drinkers to see the process at close quarters.

Small World Beers

Unit 10, Barncliffe Business Park, Near Bank, Shelley, West Yorkshire, HD8 8LU;
P: 01484 602805; W: smallworldbeers.com;
E: info@smallworldbeers.com; F/T: @smallworldbeers

The brewery's own borehole sources mineral water from the picturesque Barncliffe Valley, providing the liquor for a 20-barrel brewery established in 2013, which prides itself on deriving a high flavour profile from beers of relatively moderate strength.

They include the crisp, flaxen **Barncliffe Bitter** (3.7%), the more noticeably sharp and hoppy **Spike's Gold** (4.4%) and the more full-bodied fruity pale **Twin Falls** (5.2%) and the full-flavoured **Long Moor Pale** (3.9%). But the standout beer is the dry and toasty **Thunderbridge Stout** (5.2%) which draws its sweetness from chocolate malts – and has garnered a string of awards. A changing roster of seasonals and specials keeps things interesting; the golden **Winter Bank** (4%) develops surprising mango notes from its left-field hop combination. Light citric **Eleven** (4%) is brewed each year for Remembrance Day with a donation from each pint sold going to the poppy appeal fund.

A clutch of fine pubs and bars – the Tipsy Cow in Skelmanthorpe, the Flying Ferret in Shelley and the Woodman in Thunderbridge – in the picturesque, rolling valleys between Huddersfield and Barnsley, each stock Small World beers.

Spotlight Brewing

The Goddards, Goole Road, West Cowick, DN14 9DJ; P: 07713 477069;
W: spotlightbrewing.co.uk; E: ric@spotlightbrewing.co.uk;
F: @spotlightbrewing; T: @SpotlightBrew

Founded in 2018, this fabulous social enterprise uses beer to turn a spotlight on a number of learning difficulties. It's the brainchild of Ric Womersley, assistant manager at The Goddards, a residential home between Goole and Selby. Using kit salvaged from the former Glentworth Brewery, Ric gives tailored job roles to help residents develop their employment skills.

Session pale **One More** (3.9%) raises awareness of Down's Syndrome, the dark ruby, malt-forward **Bollingham Bitter** (4.4%) raises awareness of sudden death syndrome, while an ever-changing range of IPAs badged as **Spectrum** focus on autism. The seasonal blueberry and vanilla session porter **Dark Moment** (4.2%) draws attention to issues around depression. "And all the beers are lovely," says Matthew, Spotlight's head of sales.

Already these beers are taking these key social messages into pubs across Yorkshire and North Lincolnshire and several are also available in bottle. A QR code on their beermats signposts drinkers to further information about some of the issues which this brilliant business is bringing to wider attention.

Raising awareness one beer at a time – Ric Womersley, back, with Spotlight team Kevin, Neil and Matthew

Spotlight Fragile X (5.8%)

A subtle wisp of chocolatey vapour emerges as you prise off the cap from this luxurious chocolatey smoked porter which takes its name from a genetic condition that causes a range of developmental problems. Fragile X pours an opaque deep red-brown, and though the aroma is dominated by chocolate, there's more here – tobacco, smoke, leather, coffee – to make this a fascinating insight into great brewing too.

St Mars of the Desert

90 Stevenson Rd, Sheffield, S9 3XG; P: 07365 222101; W: beerofsmod.co.uk;
E: brewery@beerofsmod.co.uk; F: @stmarsbrewery; T: @beerofsmod

Massachusetts' loss is Sheffield's gain. For seven years, brewers Dann and Martha Holley-Paquette ran the Pretty Things Beer and Ale Project in downtown Boston, before relocating in 2018 to Sheffield. "We looked at a lot of places to move to," says Dann, who has been brewing since the 1990s and is one of many to have Harrogate's Daleside Brewery on his CV.

"We almost decided on a village in Normandy called St-Mars-du-

Desert, where we found a farm that was crying out to be a brewery." And though the plans changed, the curious name stuck, and was eventually appended to a couple of slightly ramshackle buildings east of the city centre which were once part of a foundry where there is now an on-site taproom for people to visit, tour, drink the beers and buy bottles to take away.

In addition to three conical fermentation vessels and a growing

range of wooden casks, the brewery includes a coolship – one of very few in the UK. These broad shallow vessels are at the heart of the lambic production process in Belgium, where they allow the wort to cool quickly and enable spontaneous fermentation by wild yeasts. So a Sheffield sour is certain to soon join the range.

Even so, the choice is likely to change regularly: "People are always looking to try something different," says Dann, but the deceptively potent cloudy pale saison **Jack D'Or** (7.3%), a regular brew from their Boston days, has all the makings of a new Sheffield favourite.

 Lupé (5.5%)

From a sweet-scented aroma right through to a booming bitter aftertaste, juicy Mandarina hops from Bavaria punch their significant weight in this full-bodied hazy golden ale. There's some toffee there too, and a tart marmalade bitterness to a beer of premium strength which is dangerously easy to drink.

Stancill Brewery

Unit 2, Oakham Drive, Sheffield, S3 9QX; P: 0114 275 2788;
W: stancillbrewery.co.uk; E: tom@stancillbrewery.co.uk; F/T: @stancillbrewery

When lifelong friends Tom Gill and Adam Hague salvaged brewing kit from the closed down Oakwell Brewery, they persuaded Oakwell's head brewer Jonny Stancill to join them at the new venture in Sheffield – and even put his name over the door.

Soft Peak District spring water goes into the production of a range of ales of sessionable strength, which is augmented by specials released monthly. The core range has long included nutty, creamy stout **Stancill Black** (3.7%), the light and floral **Stainless** (4.3%) and the crisp clean **Sheffield Pilsner** (5%) brewed with hops from Germany and the Czech Republic. Recent additions include **India** (4%), a crisp ruby ale; **Porter** (4.4%) a dark, toffee-ish refresher and **No 7**, a crisp citric pale ale.

🍺 **Barnsley Bitter** (3.8%)

For a beer of such uncomplicated beauty, the history of Barnsley Bitter is a surprisingly complex one. In the immediate post-war years, Barnsley Bitter's popularity grew from the mining communities of south Yorkshire to become a national phenomenon, eulogised by celebrity locals such as Parky and Dickie Bird.

In the seventies, Barnsley Brewery was taken over by Courage and closed down, before Oakwell Brewery started brewing a version in the 1990s from a unit on the same site. Also during the late 90s another Barnsley Bitter was being brewed in Elsecar, though the brewery closed and production was switched to Blackpool Brewery – a move unlikely to find favour in Yorkshire. Meanwhile, Dave Hughes, who had been head brewer at Elsecar, set up Acorn Brewery, whose own Barnsley Bitter has now become a local favourite.

Oakwell closed in 2013, paving the way for the establishment of Stancill's renascent dark amber ale with its nicely-rounded malt and caramel character which was immediately named Champion Beer of Yorkshire.

Steel City Brewing

The Circle, 33 Rockingham Lane,
Sheffield, S1 4FW;
W: www.facebook.com/groups/140082354063/;
E: dave.unpronounceable@gmail.com

Though it's now common practice, Steel City were among the UK's first cuckoo brewers – holding their own licence but creating their beers on other brewers' kit. Headed by self-styled Dave Unpronounceable, Steel City was set up to address a perceived lack of truly hoppy beers available in the UK: "A decade later that seems ridiculous, with a nuclear arms race of hops going on," he says.

Steel City remains a cuckoo in Lost Industry's nest, brewing irregular one-off beers, most likely to be found at Shakespeare's, The Rutland and The Crow in Sheffield. The two breweries regularly work together, as well as collaborating with other brewers from near and far; their original hop-heavy output is now interspersed with imperial stouts, sours – and the enthusiastic adoption of barrel-ageing.

 Argy Bargy (10.4%)

Amid all of today's political argy bargy, this fabulous formidable beer seems like an appropriate one to help you sleep it all away. A heavyweight get-together with Bristol's Arbor Brewery and Wales's Hopcraft spawned this jet-black, bottle-conditioned monster, a barley wine with the texture of engine oil and the musty aroma of wet woodland. On the palate there is so much rich, thick malt, black coffee and the purest dark chocolate that you can actually taste the blackness at the heart of this collaboration. The smoky aftertaste lasts and lasts, as though you've been burning branches out in the garden.

Stod Fold Brewing

Ogden, Halifax, HX2 8XL; P: 01422 245951; W: stodfoldbrewing.com;
E: Paul@stodfoldbrewing.com; F/T: @stodfold

Given how its reputation has spread, it's surprising to learn that Stod Fold has only been around since 2015. Its core ales have already gained quite a following, with distribution across around 300 individual free trade outlets, predominantly in Yorkshire. These include the simple refreshing **Gold** (3.8%), the more toffeeish and substantial **Best Yorkshire Bitter** (3.9%), substantial roasty **Dark Porter** (4.8%) and the smooth, fruity Yorkshire **Blonde** (4.3%).

    Stod Fold Pils (4.8%) is an accomplished cask ale take on the traditional central European style; the acidic aromas of the new **West American Pale** (4%) persist into a light-as-a-feather fruit cocktail on the palate, ending in a crisp dry finish.

    Seasonal beers such as the Irish oatmeal stout **Green Bullet** (4.2%) flesh out the range; a new brewery tap in Halifax's artsy Dean Clough centre is the best place to enquire after the latest.

Summer Wine Brewery

Crossley Mills, New Mill Road, Honley, Holmfirth, HD9 6QB;
P: 01484 665466; W: summerwinebrewery.co.uk;
E: info@summerwinebrewery.co.uk; T: @swbrewery

It's strange to think that the infantile misadventures of three elderly delinquents could have put a little Pennine town on the map, but much of Holmfirth's success as a tourist trap derives from the long-running TV series. The Summer Wine brewery celebrates this connection, the very name conjuring images of wrinkle-stockinged crones and scruffy pensioners. Even so, the beers produced in this name bear little resemblance to the ones Compo, Clegg and Foggy would have been drinking at the White Horse.

    Oh sure, there's restful ruby mild **Resistance** (3.7%) and zingy pale ale **Zenith** (4%) but from here the catalogue careers off into the kind of upland adventures the trio might have appreciated. There's bitter espresso stout **Barista** (4.8%), significantly hopped ruby red ale **Rouge** (5.8%) and the innovative **Cohort** (7.5%) which teams dark malt with US hops and Belgian yeast into a black rye ale. A growing list of single-hopped cask ales extends the range still further.

    The brewery celebrated its 10th anniversary towards the end of 2018 with a party at their own tap at Crossley Mills, where they revived a much earlier brew, the Hawaiian IPA **Mauna Kea** (6.2%) which derives bags of tropical fruit flavour from the addition of pineapple, mango, passion fruit, lychee and peach – as well as the hop cocktail of Mosaic, Citra and Sorachi Ace.

The double India Pale Ale **Maelstrom** (9%) is dangerously drinkable, but perhaps should be avoided if you're planning to spend the afternoon hurtling downhill in a bathtub.

Sunbeam Ales

52 Fernbank Road, Leeds, LS13 1BU; P: 07772 002437;
W: sunbeamales.co.uk; E: nigelpoustie@yahoo.co.uk; F/T: @SunbeamAles

Had brewer Nigel Poustie made his home in one of Leeds's less evocatively-named streets – South Accommodation Road or Grimthorpe Avenue maybe – he would probably have found a different way of naming his brewery. But when you live in Sunbeam Terrace and brew the beers in your garage, you may as well celebrate the address – even after you have decamped to LS13. He further honours the location with the zesty **Born in LS11** (5.1%), one of his most popular ales.

Nigel brews once a week, occasionally twice, rotating through a range of beers and some occasional seasonals.

They include juicy tropical fruit IPA **Sun Kissed** (3.7%), coffee and orange peel infused stout **Eclipse** (3.8%), and **Blinded by the Light** (4%), a winner in the session pales category in York CAMRA's LocAle awards.

Two further awards last year underline how campaign members love his milds. His **Chocolate Mild** (4.8%) was a winner at Calderdale beer festival; its **White Chocolate Mild** stablemate (4.2%) beer of the festival at Bradford. The Beehive in Shipley has given a permanent place to **Nigel's Plum Porter** (4.8%).

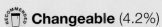 **Changeable** (4.2%)

The stylised sunset of the Sunbeam Ales pump clip forms an eye-catching image wherever it can be found. I spotted Changeable at Leeds cafe bar Slocken, and it's a beer so named because it uses a different hop variety in each iteration of the brew. This one – bright gold, smooth, and with a firm crisp bite soon giving way to a compassionate blanketing of malt – showcases the talents of Summit, and that of Nigel himself.

Tapped Brew Co

Sheffield Station, Sheaf St, Sheffield, S1 2BP; P: 0114 273 7558;
and 51 Boar Lane, Leeds, LS1 5EL; P: 0113 244 1953;
W: tappedbrewco.com; E: info@tappedbrewco.com; F/T: @tappedbrewco

A visit to the Czech Republic was the inspiration for a business whose evolving success stretches through two breweries and a chain of fabulous bars, which are serving quality ales in some prime Yorkshire locations.

Former construction engineers Jamie Hawksworth and Jonathon Holdsworth started their business importing Bernard Lager from the Czech Republic, but found real success with their first bar, Pivni in York. It was in 2009 that they took their first steps into brewing, opening the spectacular Sheffield Tap and brewhouse close to the city's railway station.

Further station taps have followed in York, Harrogate and at Euston – while a second brewery in Boar Lane, Leeds, adds keg ales to the cask beers brewed in Sheffield. Beers include the potent American-influenced IPA **Bullet** (5.9%), spicy, bubblegum wheat beer **Miami Weisse** (5.5%), light and sessionable pale ale **Jazzler** (3.9%) and the Citra hopped session pale **Citra Spark** (4%).

Specials, plus an evident passion for collaborations with other breweries, shake up the range on a regular basis.

Sheaf Street Pale (4.5%)

This new pale ale, named after the brewery's Sheffield location, was added to the Tapped range in 2018 by head brewer Nick Marchant. It follows work by boss Jamie Hawksworth to customise the brew kit to allow greater control of the hop characteristics in the beers. This one really showcases the talents of Mosaic and Centennial pale ale, with its aromas of pineapple and mango and the more bitter nature of grapefruit in the taste, in a beautifully-balanced, sessionable pale.

Tarn 51 Brewing

Robin Hood, 10 Church Road, Altofts, WF6 2NJ; P: 01924 892911;
W: tarn51brewing.co.uk; E: realale@tarn51brewing.co.uk; F/T: @tarn51brewing

The Robin Hood, Wakefield CAMRA's pub of the year in 2015, is probably the best place to sample the produce from Tarn 51's three-barrel brewery which is housed in a new building next to the pub. Here, a new Tarn Tap, where you can sample the brews right next to the brew kit, was due to start accepting visitors for private functions from the summer of 2019. Core beers include **Altofts Blonde** (4%), the very dark and surprisingly liquoricey **Appy As A Pig In Stout** (4.2%) and their Christmas imperial stout **Jòl** (7%), while seasonals – often given a first outing at the Robin Hood – fill out the range.

Tattoo Brew Co

Cropton Lane, Cropton, YO16 8HH; W: tattoobrewco.com;
E: info@tattoobrewco.com; F/T: @tattoobrewco

Designs by tattoo artist James Hobbs provide the eye-catching branding for this newly-established business based at the Great Yorkshire Brewery in Cropton. English hops form the backbone of session lager **Lighthouse** (3.8%), American hops bring a fruity character to American pale **5000 NM** (4.8%) while black malt and German hops are at the heart of the full-bodied **Windrose** (5%).

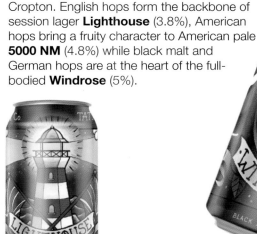

T&R Theakston Brewery

The Brewery, Masham, Ripon, HG4 4YD; P: 01765 680000;
W: theakstons.co.uk; E: info@theakstons.co.uk; F/T: @Theakston1827

Visitors are welcomed daily to Robert Theakston's tower brewery – the third site used for brewing since it had begun in 1827, but still in use today. Beer has been in constant production here since 1875; all of it passes through the original Victorian mash tun. One copper vessel is a relatively new addition, having been installed in 1936, though it was second hand, even then. **Best Bitter** (3.8%) is a quintessential Yorkshire ale, bright and golden **Lightfoot** (4.1%) has some soothing peachy flavours, while late hopping with Golding hops gives **Black Bull** (3.9%) a pronounced hoppy edge. Keg, craft keg and a host of seasonal beers fill out the roster.

One of Theakston's range of seasonal ales, **Hogshead Bitter** (4.1%) takes its name from the giant 36-gallon wooden casks, hand-crafted in the brewery by cooper Jonathan Manby. This ruby-brown ale, with its gentle effervescence and suggestions of coffee, toffee and dark cherries packs more mature fruit taste and character into its very moderate bandwidth than some brewers manage in some far stronger ales.

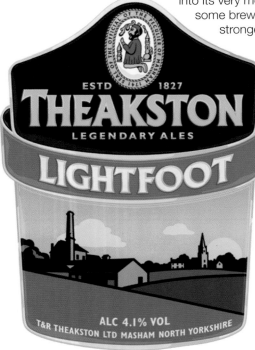

There is something faintly pantomimic about it, yet Theakston and neighbours Black Sheep remain fierce rivals, not least because of the bloodline which links the two family-owned brewers. As with their neighbours, Theakston beers are widely available across the county.

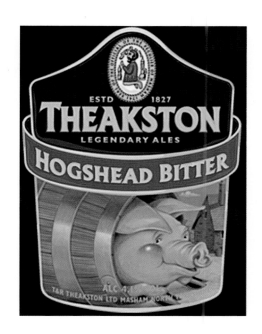

 Old Peculier (5.6%)

Sales of some big name beers are suffering in an over-crowded marketplace, yet those few with the history and cachet of Old Peculier should comfortably survive. The words "The Legend" on the label are fully justified. From its peculiar spelling to the town's seal of a crimson-clad Roger de Mowbray kneeling in apparent supplication, Theakston Old Peculier is every inch a Yorkshire legend.

This deep red-brown ale has less of a significant aroma than you might expect from a beer of 5.6% ABV, and yet it more than compensates with a full-on assault on the palate. Smooth and full-bodied, it blends rich, dried fruit, Christmas cake flavours with the the woody, grainy, almost nutty nature of the malts and caramels and just a suggestion of black pepper, which persists into a long aftertaste that develops in sufficient bitterness to make you eager to down still more. To taste it is to commune with history.

Three Fiends Brewhouse

Brookfield Farm, Mill Moor Road, Meltham, Holmfirth, HD9 5LN;
P: 07810 370430; W: threefiends.co.uk; E: sales@threefiends.co.uk;
F: threefiendsbrewhouse; T: @threefiends

The fiendish trio who set up this brewery in 2015 have been friends since they met at school aged 11. They scored an early success when spicy and distinctly orangey **Bad Uncle Barry** pale ale (4.2%) was named Best Bitter at Huddersfield's Octoberfest in 2016.

The big tasting malty pale ale **Boomer** (4.3%) makes good use of hops from Australia and New Zealand, while **Moko Titi** (4.5%) is a premium session IPA, with peachy tastes to the forefront. A brewery so named inevitably produces something fiendish – **Voodoo** (6%) is a decadent double chocolate stout with a surprising late kick of chilli; **Dark Side** (5.3%) a smooth black IPA. A restless taste for variety has seen some recent interesting additions to the range – espresso stout **Panic Attack** (6.8%), straw coloured, light and refreshing New England pale ale **Bandito** (4.5%), given oats for extra body, and crisp dry-hopped kolsch **Da Rockwilder** (4.5%). Most are available in bottle.

The fiends were pressing ahead with brewery expansion plans as we went to press; a horsebox repurposed as a mobile bar allows them to spread the word further afield.

 Two Face (4%)

Perfectly named, this craft IPA offers two contrasting flavour experiences. It presents with an effervescent aroma rich with zesty, fruity notes – but then hits the palate with a surprisingly firm, decisive, almost aggressive dry bitterness. And all this from an ale of such moderate, delicate strength. If there's some two-faced drinking acquaintance who you feel might deserve a taste of their own medicine, this could be just the thing.

Three Peaks Brewery

7 Craven Terrace, Settle, BD24 9DB; P: 01729 822939

Three easy-going and appropriately named beers are the core products for Yorkshire's westernmost brewery, which was originally established by Colin and Susan Ashwell in the cellar of their home. These are vanilla accented **Pen-Y-Ghent** bitter (3.8%); light and insubstantial **Ingleborough Gold** (4%) and the slightly darker, more assertive **Whernside Pale** (4.2%). A number of occasional beers augment the selection; in 2016 a sturdy, oily **Boatman's Stout** (5%) was launched to mark the bicentenary of the Leeds-Liverpool Canal.

Though Three Peaks has a Facebook page, it has but a single post – from six years ago – apologising for the cancellation of Craven Beer festival, but I am assured the brewery is continuing to trade. Even so, a number of breweries have disappeared since the last edition of this book. I was sad to read of the closure of **Baildon Brewing,** where brewer Leigh Terry had been so welcoming during preparations for the first edition of this book. Nearby **Bradford Brewery** is another whose demise was painful; their simple, no-nonsense recipes seemed a perfect counterpoint to the multi-hopped, intensely-flavoured beers of the craft movement, but 2018 saw them empty the fermenters for the final time.

When I visited **Northallerton Brewery** in 2017 I was struck by how confident this community-owned business was of turning around their fortunes, following the closure of much-loved Wall's County Town Brewery a year before. Sadly, the venture didn't last. **Trinity Brewing**, established in an old toilet block at Wakefield's rugby stadium seems now to have been kicked into touch.

Some have made way for others to take their place. Darkland brew where **Boothtown** once thrived, **Moorside's** premises are now home to Turning Point. **Bridge Brewery** has moved from Holmfirth to Lancashire, while **Beak** has gone still further afield, establishing new premises in Sussex.

Others which seem to have gone quiet include **Crafty Dog** (East Marton), **Fresh Island**, **Here Be Monsters** and **Bear North** (Holmfirth), **Little Shed** (Thorp Arch), **Aire Heads** (Goole), **Briscoe's** (Otley), **Whippet**, **Bobage** and **Golden Owl** (Leeds), **Bridestones** (Hebden Bridge), **Emmanuales**, **Harthill Village** and **North Union** (Sheffield), **Norland** and **Landlord's Friend** (Halifax), **Steampunk** (Allerton Bywater), **Hamelsworde** (Hemsworth), **Hedge Row** and **Salamander** (Bradford), **James & Kirkman** (Pontefract), **Two Roses** (Barnsley), **Twisted Angel** (North Newbald) and **Little Brew** (York).

Hopefully for at least some of these, it is merely a pause, rather than an ending.

Three Valleys Brewery

290-292 Rochdale Road, Todmorden, OL14 7PD; P: 07736 061150;
W: threevalleysbrewery.co.uk; E: threevalleysbrewery@yahoo.com;
F: @threevalleysbrewery

New owners Chris Leyland and Chris Duerden

For 15 years, an eye-catching pink beer shop and gallery on Rochdale Road in Todmorden was the only outlet for Barearts' bottled beers. Following a long break after a bereavement the business was re-named by home brewers Chris Duerden and Chris Leyland, who have established a good range of bottle conditioned beers which are sold through a number of local retailers. They include the mellow brown ale **Pennine Mystic** (4.5%) and the hearty **Brew Long** (7.9%) which is cask-aged before bottling. The eponymous hop gives a citric nature to the crisp **Cascade** (3.8%), while there is greater substance and a depth of honey and caramel to **Gold** (4.7%). The brewers have also experimented with bottle-conditioned and boxed ciders.

A courtyard behind the shop opens out onto the Rochdale Canal and the badlands of Lancashire are just a stone's throw west of here.

Tigertops Brewery

22 Oakes Street, Flanshaw, Wakefield, WF2 9LN; P: 01924 897728;
E: tigertopsbrewery@hotmail.com

One website lists over 230 different brews created by this innovative brewery, which was established by Stewart and Lynda Johnson, now of the Prince of Wales brewpub at Foxfield in Cumbria. Their friend Barry Smith is now the brewer; his day job cutting trees and verges for the local council has earned him the nickname Axeman. Barry's taste for the continental is illustrated by beers such as the wheat beers **White Max** (4.6%) and **Blanche de Newland** (4.5%) while **Alverthorpe Atom** porter (4.8%) and traditional bitter **Flanshaw Flyer** (4.4%) place him solidly back in the WF postcodes.

Timothy Taylor Brewery

Knowle Spring Brewery, Keighley, BD21 1AW; P: 01535 603139;
W: timothytaylor.co.uk; E: tim@timtaylors.co.uk; F/T: @timothytaylors

A swathe of new beers to sit alongside Taylor's time-honoured products has seen head brewer Andy Leman step out of the long shadow of predecessor Peter Eells and give his own gently-modernising stamp to a brewery which has long been resistant to change. These include the aromatic, dry hopped **Hopical Storm** (4%), the chocolate-accented **Poulter's Porter** (4.8%) and **1858** (5.3%) which takes the concept of a simple brown ale and concentrates it to premium strength, with a savage assault of coffee, dried fruit and warming brandy-like firmness.

These products of the brewer's imagination are only made commercially possible by the phenomenal success story of Taylor's core beers: the beautifully-balanced, sessionable **Boltmaker** (4%), sweet and toffee-ish **Dark Mild** (3.5%), zesty and palate-cleansing **Golden Best** (3.5%) and the rich, caramelly **Ram Tam** (4.3%).

Oaty, warming **Havercake Ale** (4.7%) honours the West Riding's links to the Duke of Wellington's Regiment with 10p from every sale now going to soldiers' charity ABF; amiable orange-and-spice refresher **Knowle Spring Blonde** (4.2%) is named after the artesian well which provides the water for all the Taylor beers.

Which is to say nothing of the iconic **Landlord** (4.3% cask, 4.1% bottle), a global phenomenon which has been Champion Beer of Britain four times and runner-up on three occasions. No other ale can come close to that record; few others can claim to have been championed by Madonna.

But the new broom has swept even here, with the label's avuncular red-waistcoated publican supplanted by his slightly chiselled great-nephew. Yet Landlord continues to look as lovely as ever – bright amber with a tight white head that releases an enticing aroma born of the cocktail of three hops thrown into the time-honoured brew. There's an earthy, bitter, marmalade nature to the taste, delicately balanced by suggestions of apple and toffee malt before this full bodied beer dies away in a long and slightly sweet finish.

By its name, its recipe, its brewery, its design and its history, Timothy Taylor Landlord is an absolute national treasure. It is England's greatest county distilled into a pint of perfection.

Cook Lane IPA (5.8%)

If this is Andy's attempt to muscle in on the hipster markets of craft ale, then its low-key labelling ensures it remains a subtle one, entirely in keeping with a brewery so old. Cook Lane references the brewery's original Victorian home, and is a fitting name for a beer which takes India Pale Ale back to its roots as an English ale, packed with home-grown ingredients. Aromatic Cascade and Chinook hops lend significant aroma to a big-bodied, bright golden ale which has a slightly oily feel on the palate, some bitter orange marmalade flavours and a crunchy Daim Bar finish. Andy's signature gives his personal imprimatur to a beer which demonstrates his determination to put his own stamp on Taylor's long and proud history.

Toolmakers Brewery

6-8 Botsford Street, Sheffield, S3 9PF;
P: 01142 454374;
W: toolmakersbrewery.com;
E: info@toolmakersbrewery.com;
T: @toolmbrewery

The toolmaking theme is entirely appropriate to an area steeped in steelmaking, and a whole host of beers build on that theme. Munich malt adds some caramel to **Lynch Pin** (4%), while there are some sweet-toothed suggestions of chocolate and liquorice to **Toffee Hammer** (4.3%) and some floral aromas to the sharp and pithy **Sonic Screwdriver** (4.2%). The on-site bar is both a brewery tap and a party venue available for hire, while the Forest Bar in Rutland Street provides a further ready route to market.

Treboom Brewery

Millstone Yard, Main Street,
Shipton-by-Beningbrough, YO30 1AA;
P: 01904 471569;
W: treboom.co.uk; E: info@treboom.co.uk;
F/T: @treboombrewery

Treboom marries the talents of York University research scientist John Lewis and Royal College of Art ceramicist Jane Blackman into a brewery of style and innovation. Their flagship beer is the ghostly pale, affably citric and nicely carbonated **Yorkshire Sparkle** (4%) while **Kettle Drum** (4.3%) is a more substantial, darker best bitter, and **Hop Britannia** (5%) celebrates the best of our home-grown hops in a deep flaxen ale with pronounced berry and currant notes. They have also turned their hand to a kolsch-style lager, **Trommel** (5.1%) – available in cans – and in the specials and seasonals a restless imaginative spirit emerges. 2019's list includes hibiscus and ginger **Bloom!** (4.2%), gin-inspired juniper and rosemary beer **Kopstoot** (4.6%) as well as the wheat beer **Myricale** (5%), flavoured with foraged bog myrtle.

🍺 Treboom Avant Garde (6%)

Bière de Garde – literally "beer for keeping" – is a strong pale ale traditionally brewed in French farmhouses during the colder months of the year, to avoid problems caused by the unpredictability of the yeast during the summer. As with the Belgian Saison style, the beers would be laid down for maturation in cellars for drinking later in the year, typically to slake the thirst of hardworking farmhands during the harvest. Avant Garde is Treboom's deep copper take on the style, and comes in large 750ml bottles attractively sealed with a cork. Its premium strength translates into a beer full-bodied in the mouth and sweet with toffee, floral and malty flavours. Though it makes use of Bouclier and Saaz hops, it is this grandiose fulsome sweetness which dominates over any serious suggestion of bitterness.

Triple Point

178 Shoreham St, Sheffield, S1 4SQ; P: 07828 131 423;
W: triplepointbrewing.co.uk; E: alex@triplepoint.beer; F: @triplepointbrew

The task of scratching off the Sentinel Brewery branding from the distinctive curvy glassware was just one which had to be completed before this city centre taproom re-opened as Triple Point in March 2019 after a long and painful hiatus. "Sentinel was great, but it cost so much to run, it wasn't sustainable," says former boss Alex Barlow, who remains as Head Brewer following a period of administration and re-structuring which has seen a change of ownership and a new management team. "I was a reluctant boss anyway. First and foremost I'm a brewer, and I didn't want to be doing everything else that a boss has to do."

In the new guise, Alex will concentrate on lagers – the Triple Point name referencing the Science, Art and Magic of brewing. "The science is our core range, the art is about trial beers and new techniques, the magic is what will come from collaborating with other brewers."

The murky amber and tropical fruit **Session IPA** (4.5%) has an initial release of juicy pineapple which soon gives way to greater bitterness. Pontefract cakes and dark malt bring colour and sweetness to the **Black Liquorice Lager**, which draws on the beers of famous Prague brewpub U-Fleku and was produced on the brewery's 50-litre experimental kit in time for opening night at the taproom.

Here, a high corrugated

Alex Barlow

roof, painted brickwork and factory lighting embrace the building's industrial purpose, re-positioning it for social use. High glass windows divide drinkers from the steel brewing vessels and fermenting tanks while taps on the bar are primed with all the latest produce. The **English Helles** (4.1%) and cask-conditioned **Gold** (4%) are likely to be regulars.

Pilsner (4.6%)

So new that its name was merely daubed across the trial cans, when I picked it up at the brewery's opening night, this crisp clean lager uses Zatec hops in homage to Czech brewing and particularly Staropramen, where Alex worked for two years. It does justice to the name – pale and aureate, crisp, thirst-quenching yet with the depth and character; dry hopping the same brew with Simcoe and Mosaic brings a craft IPA twist to the **Tropical Saison** (4.6%).

True North Brew Co

127-129 Devonshire Street, Sheffield, S3 7SB; P: 0114 272 0569;
W: truenorthbrewco.uk; E: bookings@truenorthbrewco.uk;
F/T: @truenorthbrewco

Obviously it's hard to guess at the priorities of any business, but when the website places beer after gin and coffee – and just before vodka – you do sense it's perhaps not True North's overriding consideration.

The company grew from a long-standing venues venture, adding these diverse drink production businesses along the way, and bringing them under a single name in 2016, around the same time that they stepped up from being cuckoos at Welbeck Abbey Brewery in Nottinghamshire to using their own city centre brewhouse.

From here, head brewer Dean Hollingworth supplies the group's own 11 pubs, as well as other independent venues. Czech Saaz and Tettnanger hops lend a crispness to the **Sheffield Pilsner** (5%), while an Amarillo and Simcoe bring their fruity, piney characteristics to the pale **Polaris** (4.3%).

While **Blonde** (4%) is golden, floral-scented and vanilla-accented, sessionable **Best Bitter** (3.8%) is a no-nonsense brown ale which taps the traditional end of the Sheffield market. Seasonals and collaborations offer both Dean and his customers more scope to experiment.

Truth Hurts Brew Co

City Mills, Peel Street, Morley, West Yorkshire, LS27 8QL;
E: paul@truthhurts.co.uk; F/T: @truthhurtsbrew

Formerly known as Blue Square, Truth Hurts emerged in around 2018, when beers such as the determinedly bitter **Part Time Punk IPA** (5.8%) and the tangy pale ale **King Kiwi** (6%) began to make their presence felt. Both were showcased at Morley Beer Festival over the Easter weekend in 2019.

Turning Point Brew Co

34-36 Dove Way, Kirkby Mills Industrial Estate, Kirkbymoorside, YO62 6QR;
P: 01751 431132; W: turningpointbrewco.com;
E: info@turningpointbrewco.com; F: @turningpointbrewco;
T: @turningpointbco

Natural spring water from the North York Moors gives its own character to the unfined and unfiltered ales from this brewery founded on the edge of the National Park in 2017. Though there are just two regular beers – the cookies and cream stout **Lucid Dream** (5%) and funky American pale ale **Disco King** (5.1%) – a host of seasonals and specials, several of which make their way into cans and bottles, fill out the range.

Vadum

49 High Street, Wath upon Dearne, S63 7QB; P: 07949 648633;
E: vadumbrewery@gmail.com; F: @vadumbrewery

The sharp-pointed V of the brewery logo should help this newcomer stand out from the crowd, but will likely give nightmares to anyone who became as obsessed as I did with the TV drama *The Widow*. Established late in 2018 by Roy Lomax of the Wath Tap, Vadum is cuckoo brewing at Hilltop in Conisborough, and focussing on traditional cask ale such as the light and aromatic blonde **Tribune** (4.2%), dark chestnut best bitter **Centurion** (4%) and resinous West Coast IPA **Commander** (5.2%).

Vocation Brewery

8 Craggs Country Business Park, Cragg Vale, Hebden Bridge, HX7 5TT;
P: 01422 844838; W: vocationbrewery.com; E: hebden@vocationbrewery.com;
F/T: @vocationbrewery

Vocation is one of the hippest, most happening and most inventive brewers around. Who could have predicted just a few years ago that alongside Magic Rock, they would form in the Pennine foothills this perfect little axis of craft supremacy?

Long-time beer obsessive John Hickling was a founding partner in Nottingham's Blue Monkey Brewery, and after stepping away from that project, realised he missed the challenge and craft of brewing – and established Vocation in his new home town of Hebden Bridge. Since then, punchy ales such as the dry-hopped **Bread & Butter** (3.9%) and the black IPA **Divide & Conquer** (6.5%) have struck a chord with drinkers both in the UK and on export to Spain, France, the Netherlands and Ireland. Three new fermenters have raised capacity to around 30,000 pints per week.

Other regular beers include tropical fruit American pale ale **Pride & Joy** (5.3%) and the more potent **Life & Death** (6.5%), a full-bodied cloudy premium IPA whose pineapple aroma and sheer strength lend a lovely sweetness that dulls the sharp, angular notes of its prodigious hop content. No two brews of Vocation's "ever-changing pale" **Chop & Change** (4.5%) are ever the same, as the hop variety changes with each brew. Many are available in can.

"We're all about brewing bold beers from our hilltop in Hebden Bridge and pouring punchy pints from our very own taprooms," Operations and Logistics Manager Rachael Pinder tells me. "We punch above our weight by putting good beer into good people's fridges and just letting our hop-forward, unapologetic beers do the talking. Our core collection is a constant to always come back to, while we show our creative flair through limited editions.

"We listen to our drinkers and only brew beer we're proud to put our name on. It's still our Vocation."

 ### Heart and Soul (4.4%)

The can describes this as a session IPA, and at its modest strength you could certainly sink a few, just so long as you like things on the cheek-suckingly fruity side. As soon as you pull back the ringpull, you unleash a huge grapefruit bouquet, and this hop-heavy citric assault continues onto the palate. Those who believe beers should all be beautifully translucent might balk at the rather cloudy, almost murky appearance of this pale yellow beer – but if you can cope with that, and fancy shocking your olfactory system with some intense bitterness, you might well go for this one, heart and soul.

Wensleydale Brewery

Unit 4, Badger Court, Leyburn, DL8 5BF; P: 01969 622463;
W: wensleydalebrewery.co.uk; E: geoff@wensleydalebrewery.co.uk;
F: @wensleydale_brewery; T: @wensleydale_ale

Friends Geoff Southgate and Carl Gehrman started working at the brewery in Carlton while still at school; when they took over in 2013 they were two of the youngest brewery owners in the UK at 23 and 22 respectively. 2018 saw the friends expand into new premises five miles away in Leyburn. The state-of-the-art 10-barrel brewkit can turn out 1,800 litres at a time, doubling capacity at a stroke.

Several of the beers name-check the local geography. Hazy golden **Semer Water** (4.1%) transmits pronounced citrus in both aroma and taste, while **Black Dub** (4.4%) – named after a deep, dark pool on the River Cover near ruined Middleham Castle – is a luxuriant, silky smooth oatmeal stout, packed with roasty chocolate tastes.

Falconer (3.9%) delivers distinct orange character and there's a courteousness to the way the 4.5% **Wensleydale Gold** treads gingerly across the palate, though some firm bitterness quickly asserts itself, buzzed around by significant carbonation. The aftertaste leaves a significant dryness in the back of the throat.

Seasonal specials allow Geoff and Carl to stretch themselves into some more interesting alternatives, but the brewery logo, a majestic shield with a sweeping sash and magnificent Bolton Castle in two-tone silhouette, speaks of the Yorkshire heritage and tradition this brewery is proud to uphold.

🍺 **Gamekeeper** (4.3%)

For the last couple of years I've led the judging for the beer category of the Flavours of Herriot Country awards – and this was the 2018 winner. A gun-carrying gamekeeper, striding with his dog across the heather-covered moorland, creates an attractive bucolic scene and the beer does everything you would expect from one so presented. It shimmers a deep translucent russet in the glass, with a tranquil caramel aroma, before treating the palate to a moreish malty lathering of pillowy comfort. It is as genial and avuncular as you would expect a gamekeeper to be, yet its strength is just enough to flex the full-bodied muscle he might need to deal with some troublesome poacher or frustrated Lady of the Manor. In the aftertaste some grassy notes emerge – and you soon find yourself reaching for another.

Westgate Brewery

Westgate, Wakefield, West Yorkshire, WF2 9SW; P: 01924 373328;
W: hbclark.co.uk; E: rebecca.longley@hbclark.co.uk

H B Clark is the UK drinks trade's largest independent wholesaler, a business which continued uninterrupted during the 1960s and 70s when the explosion of keg beer saw production in their own brewery halted. A new microbrewery resumed brewing in 1982 – and along with a host of other products, Clarks deliver their beers to 5,000 on-trade customers across the UK. Their flagship products are the interestingly spicy **Classic Blonde** (3.9%) and sessionable **English Pale** (4%), while their Merrie City craft beer marque has added **Atlantic Hop** (4%), and **Crystal Gold** (4.2%) to the collection.

Wetherby Brew Co.

York Road Estate, Wetherby, LS22 7SU; P: 01937 584637;
W: wetherbybrewco.com; E: info@wetherbybrewco.com;
F/T: wetherbybrewco

An on-site taproom is the ideal place to browse the range of this new micro, which was established in late 2017 in a former printworks a short walk from Wetherby town centre. Director John Fergusson previously had a hand in the launch of the excellent Quirky's in Garforth, and – just as there – Wetherby concentrates its efforts on traditional beers of sessionable strength. There's a **Blonde** (3.9%), a **Gold** (4%), an **IPA** (4.4%) and a **Porter** (4.3%) – but the only one I've caught up with so far is the refreshing, full bodied amber **Classic** (4.4%). All are also available in bottle.

Wharfe Beer

Melmerby Green Rd, Melmerby, Ripon, HG4 5NB; P: 01765 640108;
W: hambletonales.co.uk/wharfe-beer; E: office@hambletonales.co.uk;
T: @wharfebeeryorks

The sad closure of Wharfebank Brewery in 2016 robbed the Yorkshire scene of one of its better small breweries.

From his premises in Pool-in-Wharfedale, boss Martin Kellaway and his brewers had established a good reputation for some exceptional ales in both cask and bottle, of which my own favourite was the dark Camfell Flame. Each gained a reputation in the local market; an expansion into the pub scene gave Martin the opportunity to showcase all his beers on a single bar, notably at the Half Moon in Pool, close to the brewery.

Two of these beers have been given a fresh lease of life at Hambleton Brewery. But for loss of "bank" from the title, the packaging seems unchanged – and on the strength of a recent tasting of **Tether Blond** (4.1%), the quality is undiminished. It retains its fruity, zesty character which begins with some tropical fruit in the aroma before some rounded caramel sweetness emerges and a really dry finish. It's a session ale of depth, substance and character. **YIPA** (5.1%) is a classic Yorkshire take on this ancient style.

Wharfedale Brewery

16, Church Street, Ilkley, LS29 9DS;
P: 01943 609587;
W: wharfedalebrewery.com;
E: info@wharfedalebrewery.com;
F: @wharfedalebrewery;
T: @wharfedalebeer

The quaint, stone flagged and 300-year-old Flying Duck in the town centre is the best place to appraise the produce of a brewery which was set up in 2012 and remains rather in the shadow of the longer-established Ilkley Brewery.

Beers include the comfortable velvety mild **Black** (3.7%) which has some of the taste and texture of a strong but milky coffee; the refreshing, palate cleansing **Blonde** (3.9%) and the traditional, toffeeish **Bitter** (3.9%). Despite it being the Wharfedale brewpub, the Duck's nine handpulls on the bar offer a home to a changing selection of its Yorkshire rivals.

Whitby Brewery

East Cliff, Whitby, YO22 4JR; T: 01947 228871; W: whitby-brewery.com;
E: info@whitby-brewery.com; F/T: @whitbybrewery

Established in a tiny plant in 2013, Whitby Brewery expanded a few years ago, relocating to a hand-built 20-barrel brewery and micropub in the shadow of Whitby Abbey on a rugged headland overlooking the North Sea, where the shadow of Stoker hangs heavy in the air. The core range is available in both cask and bottle: the zesty and refreshing light ale **Abbey Blonde** (4.2%), toffee and liquorice-accented porter **Jet Black** (4.5%), full-bodied ruby ale **Saltwick Nab** (4.2%) and the passion fruit and grapefruity **IPA** (5.2%). **Black Death** stout has recently been uprated to a devilish 6.66%, and remains favourite on Whitby's twice-yearly Goth Weekends, when the town is overrun by black-clad seekers of darkness and Dracula.

 Whitby Whaler (4% ABV)

This hazy amber ale announces itself in appropriately dramatic fashion. Prising off the cap unleashes a riot of zestiness and you are almost expecting the cheek-sucking tang of an uber-hopped India Pale Ale. But once it arrives on the palate it shows a much softer and less bitter side, with some interesting toffee notes and a fruit character drawn from the peach and mango end of the spectrum rather than its lemon and grapefruit extremes. Yet there is depth and substance untypical of a beer of such moderate strength.

Whitefaced Beer Co

Penistone, South Yorkshire, S36 6EY; P: 07894 532456;
E: whitefaced@outlook.com; F/T: @whitefacedbeer

The whitefaced woodland sheep was the main commodity sold at
Penistone market and the skull of one unhappy beast is now the logo for
this new brewery, established in 2017 on a 1.3-barrel kit in a domestic
garage. While some new brewers ease themselves into the marketplace
through the sessionable end of the range, Whitefaced have dived right
into the deep end with the dank and piny double IPA **Juice Bigalo**
(8.6%), the hazy, spicy rye pale ale **First Flight** (7.1%), milk and oatmeal
stout **When The Light Hits The Dark** (5.6%) and the premium saison
Vorxtur (5.6%). There are some concessions to the easy-drinking end of
the market, like the juicy session pale **Painted Tile** (4%) and light-tasting
IPA **Tropical Swine** (3.9%), but even among their seasonal ales, the
mosaic-heavy double IPA **Ampted Up** (7.7%) and the eye-watering triple
IPA **Gyle 13** (12%) show this is not a brewery to do things by halves.

Whitefaced Beers are already finding their way into pubs around
Sheffield and Huddersfield, but the brewery is already looking for new
premises – including a taproom all of their own.

Wilde Child Brewing

Unit 5, Armley Rd, Leeds, LS12 2DR; P: 0113 244 6549;
W: wildechildbrewing.co.uk; E: info@wildechildbrewing.co.uk;
F: @wildechildbrewing; T: @wildechildbeer

To briefly adopt the name of one of his beers, Keir McAllister-Wilde is an Enfant Terrible of the Leeds brewing scene, confounding those of greater age and experience with his dazzling range of beers – which display a rare streak of brewing invention, while breaking many of the established rules.

Take **Instant Hobo** (9%). It's labelled a Bourbon Imperial Stout, which is probably a contradiction in terms seeing as how Imperial Stouts were brewed in London and exported to the Imperial Russian court, while Bourbon should either denote a Royal household of France and Spain, an American spirit – or a nice chunky chocolate biscuit. It doesn't seem a natural combination.

Yet by marrying a powerful stout brewed with two European hops and eight different malts to draughts of American barrel-aged whiskey, he has created a beer of such distinction it should win heaps of prizes. It pours a deep red-black with some suggestions of a malty, peaty, Scotch

whisky aroma, which is maintained into a taste of complexity and substance – damson, marzipan, black coffee and vanilla – before the bitter bite of dark chocolate takes over in the aftertaste.

Further examples include the slightly sweet IPA **Outside The Box** (5.7%) which derives its citric nature from a generous dose of mandarins, sturdy, French-hopped amber ale **Enfant Terrible** (4.3%) and the indulgently chocolatey **Hedonistic Existence** (6.3%). As his beers get stronger, Keir allows his imagination to run wild both with the names and the recipes. They include his firm black IPA **Hades Beckons** (6.66%), the doppelbock **Creature of Doom** (8.2%) and the slightly rough-at-the-edges, spice and tropical fruit beast of an IPA which he has named **Hopstrosity** (10.5%).

Strawberry cheesecake lends a surprising sweetening influence on the dark and dangerous **Forces Collide** (8.3%).

Keir established Wilde Child in a Leeds garage, and has since scaled up his home brews into a commercial operation, gaining an enviable reputation for imaginative, high-quality cask, keg and bottled ales which are making their way into pubs and specialist beer stores across the county. A recent move to an industrial unit in Armley afforded the opportunity to expand; an on-site bar is the perfect place to be dazzled by his crazy spirit of invention.

Pushing Boundaries
(8.1%)

This stretches what you might expect from an India Pale Ale, given that it reaches stratospheric strength – and there's something like two kilos of hops for every barrel of beer produced. Opening the can releases a huge mango aroma and the beer pours a pale and cloudy amber with an enthusiastic foaming head. But while I was expecting that assertive nose to translate into a huge fruit hit on the palate, there is more complexity than that – a dusty dryness, and some substantial and long-lasting bitterness conjured by the hop resins. It's not a session beer, not by any means, but it's a thoroughly enjoyable, one-off alcoholic fix.

Wishbone Brewery

2A Chesham Street, Keighley, BD21 4LG; P: 01535 600412;
W: wishbonebrewery.co.uk; E: info@wishbonebrewery.co.uk;
F/T: @wishbonebrewery

The simple wishbone emblem on diamond-shaped pump clips ensures brewer Adrian Chapman's products stand out on the bar. And there are plenty, many of them unfined and vegan friendly, including the session IPA **Nightstar** (3.7%), American-hopped red ale **Ruby Weapon** (4.9%), and hazy **Dassler** lager (4.2%) whose lime freshness derives from New Zealand's Motueka hop.

Adrian's choice of fined cask ales rotates regularly and includes the grainy, earthy **Blonde** (3.6%), roasty, toasty stout **Abyss** (4.3%) and the significantly hopped dry and fruit-juicey American IPA **Divination** (5.6%).

His micky-taking pale cask ale **Pastiche** (3.7%) features three fashionable hop varieties and was developed in response to SIBA's efforts to provide a definition for craft ale. "It roughly proves the fact that to a certain extent the hops you use – or can get hold of if you have enough money – guide what beers get highly rated by drinkers," he told me. "It shows how fickle the market for en-vogue hop flavours is, you could make two technically correct beers but the one

with Citra, Simcoe and Galaxy will rate more highly."

The date and liquorice porter **Medjool** (6.3%), sweet Prince-inspired fruit beer **Raspberry Brulee** (6.5%) and beechwood-smoked **Boilerplate** (5.7%) show the brewer's taste for the quirky, the whimsical and the fun.

Zoikes (4.2%)

The name sounds like something Lord Snooty might exclaim in a moment of distress, and this wonderful American-influenced pale ale draws comic book levels of dry fruity bitterness from its cocktail of Columbus, Ekuanot and Mosaic hops. There are some crisp lemon notes to the aroma as this hazy golden ale settles beneath a substantial foaming head. The taste is packed with so much juicy fruit, grapefruit and orange pith that you might not guess at its sensibly sessionable strength.

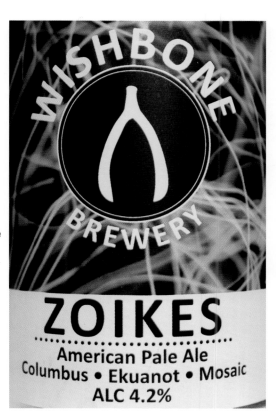

ZOIKES
American Pale Ale
Columbus • Ekuanot • Mosaic
ALC 4.2%

Wold Top Brewery

Hunmanby Grange, Wold Newton, Driffield, YO25 3HS; P: 01723 892222;
W: woldtopbrewery.co.uk; E: enquiries@woldtopbrewery.co.uk

Wold Top Brewery was founded in 2003 by Tom and Gill Mellor on their 600-acre farm high on the Yorkshire Wolds – and is now run by their daughter Kate and son-in-law, Alex. They use home-grown barley and water gently filtered by Wolds chalk and drawn from the farm's own borehole. There is a focus on sustainability and maintaining biodiversity, and on sourcing ingredients and services as locally as possible.

The brewery supplies Yorkshire pubs with a range of year-round beers and two seasonal cask ales every month – and you'll find their bottles in the supermarkets too. Fragrant **Wold Top Bitter** (3.7%) is the entry-level ale, while others include the complex gluten-free **Marmalade Porter** (5%) and **Anglers' Reward** (4%), a refreshing pale ale with some quite perfumy aromas, biscuit and caramel, fruity bitterness and a lingering aftertaste.

Thankfully devoid of parsley, sage, rosemary, thyme and gluten, the excellent **Scarborough Fair** (6%) is a beautifully sparkling IPA with fruity aromas and a taste whose bitterness mellows into spicy vanilla and black cherry.

Kate and Alex Balchin, with their twins Beth and Tilly, flanked by brewery founders Tom and Gill Mellor

 Wold Gold (4.8%)

I picked up a couple of bottles of Wold Gold on a rambling trip to East Yorkshire. The occasion was our walking group's first ever trip to the Wolds, and we had an idyllic afternoon yomping through the gently-rolling fertile landscape, a day only marginally spoiled by me tumbling down a hill and barrelling headfirst into a tree.

I should have cracked open a bottle there and then; Wold Gold would make a perfect pick-me-up. Attractively clear yellow of colour, with a soft white head, the zesty aroma soon gives way to the soft and fruity taste of a lightly-carbonated beer that bathes the palate in bitterness and spice. The experience is completed by some interesting peaty earthy notes in a remarkable finish that lasts and lasts.

Wold Gold took the gold award in the Premium Bitters, Bottle and Can category at the 2019 SIBA National Independent Beer Awards in Liverpool.

York Brewery

12 Toft Green, York, YO1 6JT; P: 01904 621162;
W: york-brewery.co.uk; E: enquiries@york-brewery.co.uk; F/T: @yorkbrewery

Though not far beyond its 21st birthday, York Brewery is now a veteran of the local brewing scene, compared to the dozens of brewpubs and micros which have opened in recent years.

Though York's beers are now widely distributed across Yorkshire and Lancashire, the surest place to browse their impressive range is at one of their own pubs, places like The Last Drop and Three Legged Mare in York – both named to honour methods of capital punishment – and Foley's Alehouse in Leeds.

Crisp, dry and refreshing **Guzzler** is very much the session beer, whether it's the 4% version in bottle or the 3.6% brew which they send to the pubs. It's the essence of an easy-drinking pale ale, with a suggestion of tangerine in the aroma, a crisp blast of fresh fruit with a touch of carbonation and a slight buttery silkiness, before a dusty dryness emerges right at the finish, just tempting you to drink some more.

Yorkshire Terrier (4.2%) settles to a bright attractive golden colour, with a thinnish head that soon fritters away. There are some short-lived zesty notes to the aroma, but its true character really comes out on the palate where an appropriate, terrier-like bite and some easy carbonation unleash the autumnal crispness of apples and the soft reassurance of caramel.

Several of the brewery's ales namecheck this historic city's ancient past – **Centurion's Ghost** (5.4%) is a dark, smooth and mellow mild, creamy plummy **Black Bess** (4.2%) a delicious wintry oatmeal stout. Crisp and fruity **Legion IX** (6.5%) is their premium pale ale, while there is a fruitcake maltiness to high-octane dark ale **Imperium** (7.5%).

A period of administration in December 2018 briefly threatened an end to this much-loved local brewery. Its resultant acquisition by Black Sheep is good news for both parties, ensuring these beers continue to reach their thirsty customers across the north, while allowing the Masham brewery to finally dip its toes into the retail trade.

 Minster Ale (4.2%)

The medieval biblical tableaux of the Mystery Plays are an important part of the vivid tapestry that makes up this ancient city. Traditionally each of the play's 48 scenes was staged by one of the city's craft guilds; the local coopers who furnished brewers with wooden beer barrels were, perhaps appropriately, responsible for the Fall of Man.

The link between brewing and the ecclesiastical life of the city continues through this zesty flaxen ale, slightly effervescent, yet packed with more genuine fruity, hoppy bitterness than you might expect from an ale of such modest strength. The aroma has suggestions of cider, but peach and apricot take over once it hits the palate, before a long significant aftertaste rounds off a wholly splendid experience.

MINSTER ALE

CRISP AND REFRESHINGLY BITTER

ALC **4.2%** VOL

AN AWARD WINNING BREWERY WITHIN THE CITY WALL

WWW.YORK-BREWERY.CO.UK

SINCE 1996
YORK BREWERY

YORKSHIRE TERRIER

RICH AND CREAMY YORKSHIRE BITTER

SINCE 1996
YORK BREWERY

GUZZLER

GOLDEN, CRISP AND REFRESHING

Yorkshire Brewing

Brewery Wharf, 70 Humber Street, Hull, HU1 1TU; P: 01482 618000;
W: yorkshirebrewing.co.uk; E: info@yorkshirebrewing.co.uk;
F/T: @YorkshireBrewCo

Close to Hull's historic waterfront, in former fruit market warehouses rediscovered by the city's burgeoning Arts Quarter, Yorkshire Brewing is going from strength to strength. The recent launch of its spectacular new Taphouse venue has placed it right at the heart of an £80m regeneration.

Taphouse is East Yorkshire's largest brewpub and combines a working brewery with a high-quality bar offering almost 40 draught craft beers, lagers and ciders, as well as an extensive range of bottled and canned beers. Drinkers can watch the brewers at work in the rear of the bar, while regular tours allow them to get up-close and personal with the process.

Yorkshire Brewing's sizeable range includes multi-hopped **Oregon Gold** (4.5%) with its notably refreshing melon aftertaste; sessionable hoppy and bitter **Mosaic** (4.2%) whose tangerine, berry and tropical fruit notes demonstrate the dimensions of this popular hop variety; and West Coast influenced IPA **Waverider** (5.5%).

There is clearly a thirst for innovation at work here: rum adds to the complexity of dark seasonal ale **Old Ebenezer** (4.5%); while **Polar Beer** (6%) gains its oaky, rich fruity taste from maturation in old bourbon casks. And there's an eagerness to cast fresh fruit into the brewkit – fresh blackberries enrich **Blackjack** stout (4.5%), soft summer fruits enhance Belgian-influenced **Strawberry Blonde** (4.8%) and **Raspberry Tipple** (4.8%), oranges add extra spike to wheat beer **Moondance** (4.5%).

The Taphouse brewery is shared with Bone Machine Brew Co (see page 26) and has the capacity to brew more than 15,000 pints a week and store over 30,000 pints in its holding tanks. This new facility will offer these two innovative breweries the capacity to spread themselves into a host of brewing styles. Some beers will be aged over a period of time in oak casks for greater maturity; some will be blended with other beers or enhanced with spirits. Others will harness wild yeast to produce lambic sours.

Says boss Guy Falkingham: "We want to maximise the appeal of having a working brewery and bar under the same roof. We've teamed up with Bone Machine because we have a shared passion for artisan brewing. Together we can offer a great range of brews for our in-house customers and a growing number of wholesale and retail outlets."

Mutiny (3.6%)

This dark, coffee-ish ale blends oats and a host of malts in a 1750 London Porter recipe – and was named 'Best Dark Ale in Wooden Cask' in 2018. Beyond its sleepy malty characteristics there is some sweetness, a suggestion of burnt pastry and perhaps just the mellow fruitfulness of damson.

Yorkshire Dales Brewing Company

Abbey Works, Askrigg, DL8 3BJ; P: 01969 622027;
W: yorkshiredalesbrewery.com; E: rob@yorkshiredalesbrewery.com;
F: @yorkshiredales.brewery; T: @yorkshiredalesb

Over a dozen years and more, brewer Robert Wiltshire has created hundreds of different brews – cask, unfiltered craft keg and bottle conditioned – each with its own unique recipe. His success has seen the beers distributed widely across Yorkshire and an export deal to Germany, while a move into new premises has created a new American-led microbrewery experience. Several of the permanent beers reflect that influence, including the assertively citric American session ale **Butter Tubs** (3.7%), peachy **Nappa Scar** (4%), helles-style **Muker Silver** (4.1%) and **Askrigg Ale** (4.3%), an IPA whose big flush of tropical fruit is derived from Amarillo hops. Two more traditional British beers, the brown ale **Askrigg Bitter** (3.8%) and dark mild **Drover's Arms** (3.9%) complete the regular catalogue.

🍺 Garsdale Smokebox (5.6%)

Smoky rauchbiers originated in Germany. Legend tells us that a brewhouse survived a fire at Bamberg's medieval cathedral in Northern Bavaria, but the malt had been exposed to the smoke, creating a beer which remains popular with tourists and locals alike.

To ensure authenticity, Yorkshire Dales Brewing imported malt from Bamberg which had been dried over open fires made from beechwood logs. Sometimes native rauchbiers can be too extreme, too packed with acrid smoke that any nuance of flavour is choked out of the brew. But here we find a lighter touch that lets all those flavours breathe.

The smoke is unmistakeable all the same. As you prise off the cap you are struck with bonfire flavours, black treacle, fireworks and perhaps a whiff of cordite in a jet black beer with a thin ivory head.

While this sense of the dark days of autumn is maintained on the palate, the influence of sweet sherry, black cherries and dark chocolate can also be sensed in a brew which would provide an interesting counterpoint to Wensleydale's moist and crumbly cheese.

Hops are doubtless used somewhere in the brew, yet their influence is dialed right down in a bottle conditioned beer of substance, strength, practically zero bitterness and very little carbonation.

Yorkshire Heart Brewery

The Vineyard, Pool Lane, Nun Monkton, York, YO26 8EL; P: 01423 330716;
W: yorkshireheart.com; E: sales@yorkshireheart.com;
F: @yorkshireheartvineyard; T: @yorkshire_heart

With a cider press being added to its vineyard and brewery, Yorkshire Heart has most of the major booze options covered; a popular visitor centre has enhanced its reputation as a top tourist attraction. The name is ripe for beery puns, which include the smooth and coffeeish mild **Darkheart** (4%) and the chestnut brown toffee-ish session ale **Hearty Bitter** (3.7%). **Silverheart** (4%) is a pale golden effervescent IPA, crisp and bright, only moderately bitter, and an effective palate-cleansing refresher.

🍺 **Blackheart Stout** (4.8%)

This full-bodied liquoricey stout looks absolutely perfect – impenetrably jet black, with a firm ivory head that retains its shape as the level falls. There is some attractive dark chocolate to the aroma, and on the palate Blackheart provides a wispy smokiness and a silky, luxurious layering of sweet vanilla and tobacco.

Zapato

Holme Mills, Slaithwaite Road, Marsden, HD7 6LS; P: 01484 521954;
W: zapatobrewery.co.uk; E: info@zapatobrewery.co.uk; F/T: @zapatobrew

Beer consultant Matt Gorecki, a big noise behind beer festivals in Manchester and Leeds, cut his teeth with North Bar group before establishing his own cuckoo brewery, using spare capacity at Northern Monk, Kirkstall and Atom and named after Mexico's anarcho-leftist Zapatistas. Now installed in a former textile mill west of Huddersfield, Matt has an attractive taproom and beer garden to the front and – by the time this book goes to print – a brewery to the rear. It's here that he will finally establish his core range on home soil, and take the opportunity afforded by his own brewkit to experiment.

Double Zero (4%) is "our steady away pale ale," says Matt; part of each brew will go into cask. Citra hops form the base of **Zapato Pale** (5.5%) though the character of the beer will change with different dry-hopping recipes while blackberries and raspberries add colour and just a gentle tartness to the **Beaucoup Weiss** (3%).

He describes export-style porter **Doom** (6%) as a "base beer" to which he can add flavourings depending on his mood – recent iterations

include a black bean version and one made with honey and grape molasses. Naturally-fermenting saisons and fruit beers, and an ever-changing choice of IPAs will all provide further proof of a fervent imagination and a brewery bursting with promise.

Delegate Zero (6.2%) is a hoppy stout using kola nuts and based on a beer which Matt originally created with Brewdog as a one-off beer for his wedding to Alice Porter. The Scots brewery so liked the results and her serendipitous name they

ended up putting it on general sale.

Matt was keen to use his alphabetical position to have this book's last word on the state of Yorkshire's brewing industry. "It's an exciting time – and one that is constantly evolving, with brewers drawing their influences from all over the world. Whether we can sustain this number of breweries long term is open to question, but I am absolutely certain that the best ones will survive."

Nelson Pils (6.3%)

This lovely warming pilsner demonstrates some of the clear benefits of collaboration. Created with Hartlepool's German-inspired brewer Donzoko, this hearty, copper-coloured ale is the antithesis of the standard cold, refreshing Pils. Doubtless this substance and character is at least partly the product of its premium strength: "We were looking for something around 5.5%," says Matt. "Perhaps we just got carried away."

Acknowledgments

Thanks are due to all those breweries which were kind enough to help me by submitting details for inclusion in the book – and particularly those who welcomed me to their premises, and obviously also those who supplied welcome packages of beer!

A number of branch officials of the Campaign for Real Ale have been especially helpful with this second edition. Dave Pickersgill of the Sheffield branch should be singled out for particular praise for his endless helpful suggestions, and for making so many of his pictures available to me.

Paul Ainsworth of the Barnsley branch and John Hartley of the Halifax and Calderdale branch deserve my particular thanks for giving of their time and sharing so much of their knowledge of a number of breweries in their areas. Also thanks to Kate Ahern (Bradford), Steve Pynegar (Doncaster), Mike Roebuck (Heavy Woollen), Bob Tomlinson (Huddersfield), Bob Wallis (Wakefield), Peter Judge (Halifax and Calderdale) and Colleen Holliday (Keighley and Craven) for their support.

Jules Gray, the driving force behind Sheffield Beer Week, was also kind enough to offer her expert guidance – and thanks also for their various contributions to Martin Kellaway, Andy Pollard and Mike Hampshire – and to Tom Fozard of Rooster's Brewery for being generous enough to once again support the project with an advertisement.

Thanks also to David Burrill at Great Northern Books for his enthusiasm for the project – and to my wife Katrina for accompanying me to so many of the breweries featured, and for regular supplies of coffee and encouragement during the writing and editing of the text.

Picture credits

The majority of photographs in this book were taken by myself, though Abbeydale (p6), Blue Bee and Kelham Island Tavern (p25), Dead Parrot (p49), Loxley (p103), Neepsend (p118-9), St Mars of the Desert (p162 top and p163 top), Triple Point Sky's Edge (p180) are all by Dave Pickersgill.

Anthology (p12) is by Mike Massen, The Cardigan Arms (p88) is courtesy of Kirkstall Brewery and Tetley's Pale Ale (p93) is courtesy of Leeds Brewery. The new images of Meanwood Brewery (p108-9) are by Jeremy Kelly though the image of the brothers celebrating after being handed the keys is by Josh Eliff. The Nomadic mural (p120) is by Christine Jopling; The Nook (p123) by courtesy of Yorkshire Post Newspapers; Northern Monk (p129-9) by Giles Smith.

The Black Sheep brothers (p23), Darkland (p48), Eagles Crag (p51), Harrogate Brewing (p68-69), Ilkley's head brewer (p78), Jolly Boys (p83), Sue and Wim of Little Valley (p98), Ross and Katie of Nomadic (p121), the Rooster's Taproom (p147), Saltaire Brewery (p150-152), Steel City (p165 top), Tapped (p167), Three Valleys (p174), Treboom Sparkle (p178-9), Whitby beers (p190), the Balchin and Mellor families (p197) and Yorkshire Brewing Taphouse (p201) are each by courtesy of their respective breweries. Though many of the bottle images were again by myself, thanks also to the many breweries and websites whose advice and resources helped to source some of the pump clip, logo and beer bottle image pictures.